ULTIMATE CROSS WORDS

OVER 450 PUZZLES

hinkler

SOLVING TIPS

This book is in US English, so you can use the Merriam-Webster Dictionary for help, which can be found in stores or online at www.merriam-webster.com.

If you are used to UK, Canadian, or Australian English, look out for the following conversions to US English:

- "-ise" becomes "-ize"
E.g. realize and digitize

- "-our" becomes "-or"
E.g. humor, neighbor, and favorite

- "-re" becomes "-er"
E.g. theater and fiber

- "-ll" becomes "-l"
E.g. counselor and filet

- "-ce" becomes "-se"
E.g. defensive and license

- "-s" becomes "-z"
E.g. cozy and analyze

- "-gue" becomes "-g"
E.g. dialog and analog

hinkler

Published by Hinkler Books Pty Ltd 2019
45–55 Fairchild Street
Heatherton Victoria 3202 Australia
www.hinkler.com

Puzzles © Clarity Media 2019
Design © Hinkler Books Pty Ltd 2019
Cover Design: Hinkler Studio

ISBN: 978 1 4889 4001 9

Printed and bound in China

INSTRUCTIONS

If you're not familiar with crossword puzzles, here are some tips for how to solve them.

The goal is to solve the clues and write in the answers, letter by letter, into the blank squares in the grid. The numbered clues will direct you to fill in the answers both across and down the grid. Fill in the obvious answers first and then look again at the puzzle clues—there may be an easy answer you didn't notice or one that's easier now because some letters have been filled in.

Numbers in parentheses after each clue reveal the number of letters in each answer, matching the number of spaces in the grid. Multiple numbers separated with a comma indicate multiple words; numbers separated with a hyphen indicate hyphenated words.

Clues ending in "(abbrev.)" indicate that the solution is an abbreviation; clues ending in "(anag.)" indicate that the solution is an anagram; if there is "(pl.)"after the clue it means the answer is a plural, while clues ending in "(inits.)" indicate that the solution is a set of initials.

Some handy tricks are checking if an "s" in the last position works for standard plural-words clues and "ed" for past-tense clues. Keep working through the list of clues and, if you're stumped, try again later! Sometimes you just need a break for your brain to retrieve the answer.

CROSSWORD 1

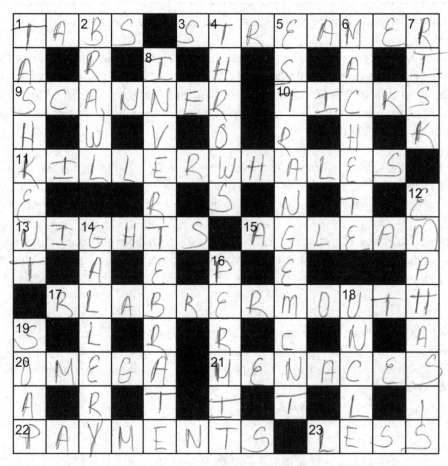

Across

1 Bats (anag.) (4)
3 Pennant (8)
9 Data input device (7)
10 Parasitic arachnids (5)
11 Orcas (6,6)
13 Periods of darkness (6)
15 Shining (6)
17 Gossip (12)
20 Last Greek letter (5)
21 Threatens (7)
22 Remittances (8)
23 Not as much (4)

Down

1 Capital of Uzbekistan (8)
2 Uproarious party or fight (5)
4 Propels through the air (6)
5 Separation; alienation (12)
6 Knife (7)
7 Chance taken (4)
8 Lacking a backbone (12)
12 Importance; stress (8)
14 Where artwork is displayed (7)
16 Allow (6)
18 Male relation (5)
19 Substance used for washing (4)

Across

1 Run-down and in poor condition (6)
5 Deep hole in the ground (3)
7 Effluent system (5)
8 Adult (5-2)
9 The entire scale (5)
10 Deceive (8)
12 Fish-eating bird of prey (6)
14 Thick innermost digits (6)
17 Most saccharine (8)
18 Hoarse (5)
20 Enthusiastic reception (7)
21 European country (5)
22 Small spot (3)
23 Protective headgear (6)

Down

2 Extremely shocking things (7)
3 Twining plant (8)
4 Slender woody shoot (4)
5 Sum added to interest (7)
6 Rags (7)
7 Used up; exhausted (5)
11 Cord for fastening footwear (8)
12 Land with fruit trees (7)
13 Carry on (7)
15 Made to individual order (7)
16 Faint (5)
19 Period of 365 days (4)

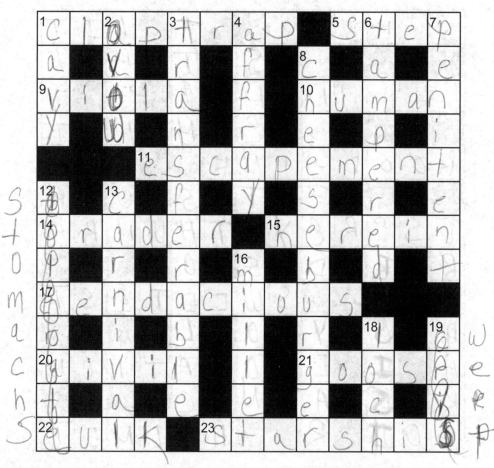

Across

1 Nonsense (8)
5 Pace (4)
9 Musical instrument (5)
10 Mortal (5)
11 Mechanism in a clock (10)
14 Person who buys and sells (6)
15 Within this context (6)
17 Dishonest (10)
20 Polite and courteous (5)
21 Large waterbird (5)
22 Be in a huff (4)
23 Spacecraft (8)

Down

1 Guinea pig (4)
2 Affirm solemnly (4)
3 Capable of being moved (12)
4 Disturbance (6)
6 Interfered with (8)
7 Expressing remorse (8)
8 Fast food item (12)
12 Puts up with (8)
13 Festival (8)
16 Small-seeded annual cereal (6)
18 Scottish lake (4)
19 Shed tears (4)

CROSSWORD 4

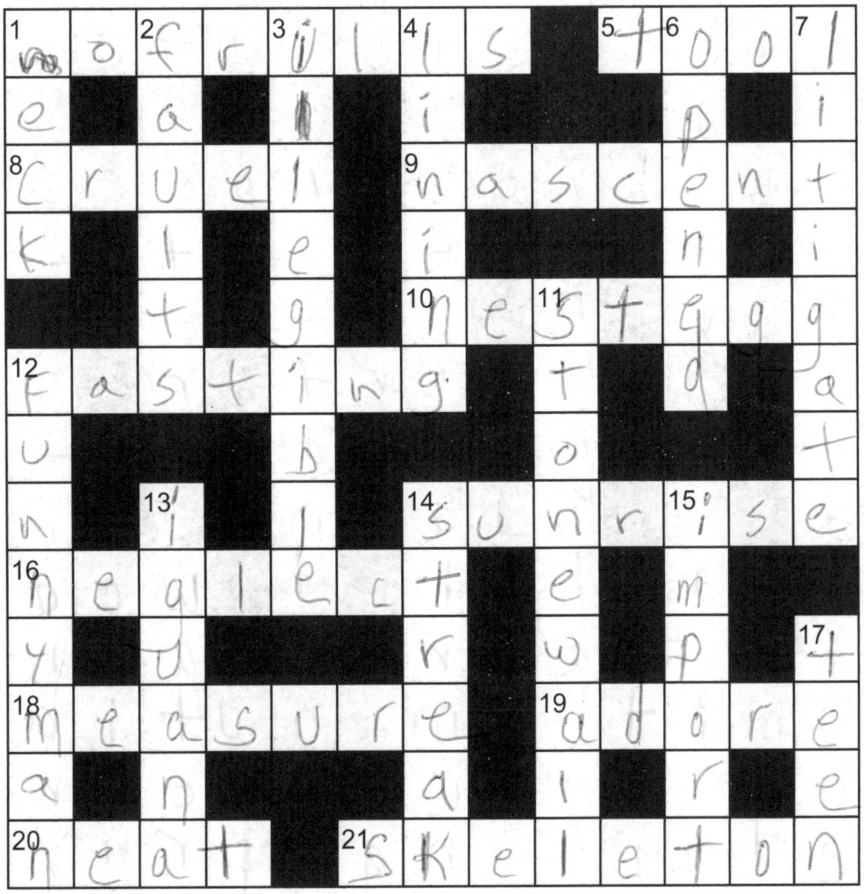

Across

1 Low-cost travel package (2-6)
5 Useful implement (4)
8 Excessively mean (5)
9 Beginning to exist (7)
10 Savings for the future (4,3)
12 Abstaining from food (7)
14 First light (7)
16 Fail to care for (7)
18 Ascertain dimensions (7)
19 Worship; venerate (5)
20 Tidy (4)
21 The bones of the body (8)

Down

1 Narrow strip of land (4)
2 Technical problems (6)
3 Unreadable (9)
4 Protective layer (6)
6 Took the lid off a jar (6)
7 Take legal action (8)
11 Obstruct a process (9)
12 Male comedian (8)
13 Large lizard (6)
14 Long thin line or band (6)
15 Bring into a country (6)
17 Adolescent (4)

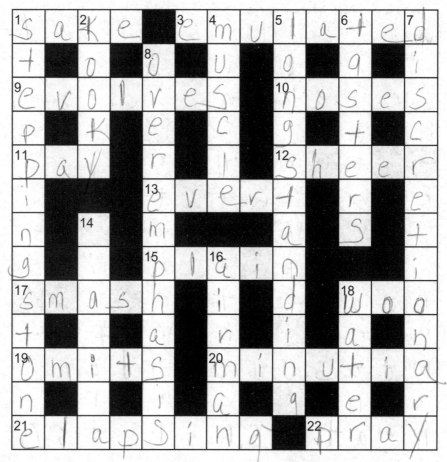

Across

1 Japanese beverage (4)

3 Copied (8)

9 Changes gradually (7)

10 Facial protuberances (5)

11 Remuneration (3)

12 Remove wool from sheep (5)

13 Turn inside out (5)

15 Clear and apparent; obvious (5)

17 Break into pieces (5)

18 Court (3)

19 Leaves out (5)

20 The small details of something (7)

21 Passing (of time) (8)

22 Address a deity (4)

Down

1 Any means of advancement (8,5)

2 Eccentric (5)

4 Brawn; strength (6)

5 Having existed for a considerable time (4-8)

6 Food samplers (7)

7 Available for use as needed; optional (13)

8 Excessive stress (12)

14 Musical wind instrument (7)

16 Pilot (6)

18 Liquid essential for life (5)

Across

1 Innovative or pioneering (7,4)
9 Hard and brittle (5)
10 Moved quickly on foot (3)
11 Imbibe (5)
12 Long-handled spoon (5)
13 Manner; mental state (8)
16 Roomy (8)
18 Flatten on impact (5)
21 Insect grub (5)
22 Deciduous tree (3)
23 Lively Bohemian dance (5)
24 Stargazers (11)

Down

2 Raises (7)
3 Permits to travel (7)
4 Denial (anag.) (6)
5 Remove from school (5)
6 Pierced by a bull's horn (5)
7 Children's game (4-3-4)
8 Needless (11)
14 Praise strongly (7)
15 Messenger (7)
17 What bees collect (6)
19 Young sheep (5)
20 Come to a point (5)

Across

1 Capital of the Philippines (6)
7 Partition inside a ship (8)
8 Came across (3)
9 Contaminate (6)
10 Crack (4)
11 Units of heredity (5)
13 Adopt or support a cause (7)
15 Smart; chic (7)
17 Moves through the air (5)
21 Swallow eagerly (4)
22 Sufficient (6)
23 Ancient boat (3)
24 Aided (8)
25 Move apart; open out (6)

Down

1 Conveying by gestures (6)
2 Country (6)
3 Monastery church (5)
4 Snobbish (7)
5 Form of carbon (8)
6 Blunders (6)
12 Omission from speech of
   superfluous words (8)
14 Takes a firm stand (7)
16 Hackneyed statement (6)
18 Breathe in (6)
19 Wagered (6)
20 Incites (5)

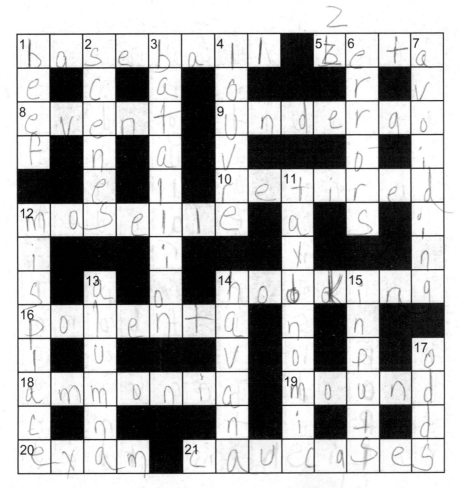

Across

1 Sport popular in America (8)
5 Sixth Greek letter (4)
8 Happening (5)
9 Be subjected to (7)
10 Stopped working (7)
12 European river (7)
14 Illegal action in ice hockey (7)
16 Cornmeal (7)
18 Pungent gas (7)
19 Rounded mass (5)
20 School test (4)
21 Political meetings (8)

Down

1 Cow meat (4)
2 Parts of a play (6)
3 Large body of troops (9)
4 Famous French museum (6)
6 Mistakes (6)
7 Evading (8)
11 Related to classification (9)
12 Lose (8)
13 Former female pupil (6)
14 Capital of Cuba (6)
15 Contributes information (6)
17 Chances of winning (4)

Across

1 Film that makes one laugh (6)
4 Annul (6)
9 Military attack or raid (7)
10 Flatter (7)
11 Horse (anag.) (5)
12 Assisted (5)
14 Touch on; mention (5)
15 Liquid part of fruits (5)
17 Plants of a region (5)
18 Polishing (7)
20 Lifting with difficulty (7)
21 Enjoy greatly (6)
22 Joined together (6)

Down

1 Unrefined (6)
2 Midwestern US state (8)
3 Put out (5)
5 Having sharp corners (7)
6 Closing section of music (4)
7 Myth (6)
8 Fear in front of an audience (5,6)
13 Removing from office (8)
14 Lives in (7)
15 Speak rapidly (6)
16 Fell behind (6)
17 Picture border (5)
19 Fencing sword (4)

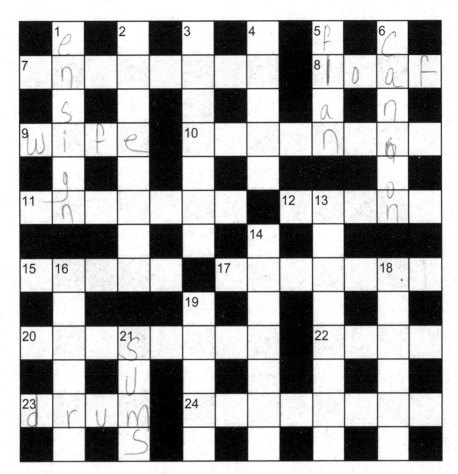

Across

7 Assisting the memory (8)
8 Foal (anag.) (4)
9 Married woman (4)
10 Most influential or important (8)
11 Ennoble (7)
12 Amazes (5)
15 Misgiving (5)
17 Blood relative (7)
20 Subsidiary (8)
22 Display (4)
23 Percussion instrument (4)
24 Make weak (8)

Down

1 Banner or flag (6)
2 Relating to an empire (8)
3 Contemptuously (7)
4 Rascal (5)
5 Open tart (4)
6 Large artillery gun (6)
13 Metallic element used in light bulbs (8)
14 Strengthen (7)
16 Unfold (6)
18 Mythical monsters (6)
19 Comedian (5)
21 Adds (4)

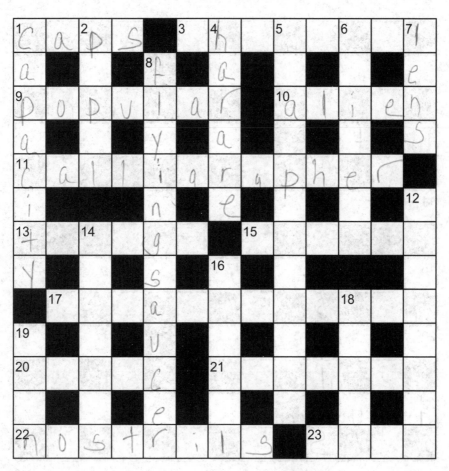

Across

1 Hats (4)
3 Pertaining to the body (8)
9 Liked by many people (7)
10 Horror film directed by Ridley Scott (5)
11 Someone skilled in penmanship (12)
13 However (6)
15 Instrumental piece of music (6)
17 Mentally acute (5-7)
20 Frenzied (5)
21 Changed or modified (7)
22 Channels of the nose (8)
23 Catch sight of (4)

Down

1 Maximum number a stadium can hold (8)
2 Proceeding from the pope (5)
4 Capital of Zimbabwe (6)
5 Having an acrid wit (5-7)
6 Grotesque monster (7)
7 Part of a camera (4)
8 UFO (6,6)
12 Frankly (8)
14 Elongated rectangles (7)
16 Attack (6)
18 Edits (anag.) (5)
19 So be it (4)

Across

1 Striped animals (6)
5 Exclamation of amazement (3)
7 Lean or thin (5)
8 Room used for preparing food (7)
9 Finds agreeable (5)
10 Trade (8)
12 Guardian (6)
14 Treat indulgently (6)
17 Put into action (5,3)
18 E.g. from Athens (5)
20 Is present at (7)
21 Thread-weaving machines (5)
22 Month of the year (3)
23 Spreads out and apart (6)

Down

2 Perfect example of a quality (7)
3 Accomplished (8)
4 Cry out (4)
5 Saturday and Sunday (7)
6 Edge of a road (7)
7 Repast (5)
11 Wedge to keep an entrance open (8)
12 Domain (7)
13 Old (7)
15 Clothes for washing (7)
16 Heroic tales (5)
19 Intertwined segment of rope (4)

CROSSWORD 13

Across

1 Regretted (4)
3 Roman leaders (8)
9 20th letter of the Greek alphabet (7)
10 Stringed instrument (5)
11 Thing that fails to work properly (3)
12 Refute by evidence (5)
13 Strength (5)
15 Small restaurants (5)
17 Held on to something tightly (5)
18 Belonging to him (3)
19 General hatred (5)
20 Spanish beverage (7)
21 Capital of Jamaica (8)
22 Sums together (4)

Down

1 Without stopping; continuous (5,3,5)
2 Loosened (5)
4 Tiny fish (6)
5 Awkward (12)
6 Public transport vehicle (7)
7 Meteors (8,5)
8 International multi-sport event (7,5)
14 Gathering of old friends (7)
16 Ludicrous failure (6)
18 Gave a job to (5)

Across

1 Renown (4)
3 Rebellious (8)
9 Milk sugar (7)
10 Chubby (5)
11 Spoke softly (5)
12 Prior (7)
13 Entry pass (6)
15 Doorway (6)
17 Snared (7)
18 Relating to sound (5)
20 Academy award (5)
21 Traditional piano keys (7)
22 Firmness (8)
23 Feeling of resentment or jealousy (4)

Down

1 Congratulations (13)
2 Very masculine (5)
4 Not level (6)
5 Imitator (12)
6 Type of optician (7)
7 In a manner that exceeds what is necessary (13)
8 Easy-going (4-8)
14 Part of a church near the altar (7)
16 Floating freely (6)
19 Condescend (5)

CROSSWORD 15

Across

1 Rose fruits (4)
3 Definite and clear (8)
9 Not tense (7)
10 Ravine (5)
11 Vain (12)
13 Hard to digest (6)
15 One's environment (6)
17 Quality of being at hand when necessary (12)
20 Type of soup (5)
21 Treachery (7)
22 Preserve or hold sacred (8)
23 Remain (4)

Down

1 Toughness (8)
2 More ashen in appearance (5)
4 Free from ostentation (6)
5 Joyously unrestrained (4-8)
6 Stations at the ends of routes (7)
7 Musical staff sign (4)
8 Device for putting out fires (12)
12 Ability to float (8)
14 Evident (7)
16 Fabric associated with Scotland (6)
18 One image within another (5)
19 Double-reed instrument (4)

Across

1 Take as being true (6)
4 Dismissed from a job (6)
9 Capital of Ontario (7)
10 Defective (7)
11 Strong thick rope (5)
12 Spear (5)
14 Thin pancake (5)
15 Type of tree (5)
17 Place providing accommodation (5)
18 Back pain (7)
20 Signs (7)
21 Give satisfaction (6)
22 Far from the target (6)

Down

1 Join or fasten (6)
2 Cleansed thoroughly (8)
3 Chop meat into very small pieces (5)
5 Disciple (7)
6 African antelope (4)
7 Move slowly (6)
8 Betray (6-5)
13 In the adjacent residence (4,4)
14 Makes (7)
15 Summon; telephone (4-2)
16 Vitreous (6)
17 Rounded protuberances on camels (5)
19 Beast of burden (4)

Across

1 Enormous (11)
9 Cook meat in the oven (5)
10 Pub (3)
11 Golf clubs (5)
12 Faithful (5)
13 Harmful in effect (8)
16 Religion (8)
18 Detection technology (5)
21 Small firework (5)
22 Gone by (of time) (3)
23 Swerves off course (5)
24 Acting out a part (4,7)

Down

2 Animal fat (7)
3 Root vegetable (7)
4 Spiny tree or shrub (6)
5 Sum; add up (5)
6 Very loud (5)
7 Designed for usefulness (11)
8 Combustible (11)
14 Epic poem (7)
15 Tar-like hydrocarbon (7)
17 Ill (6)
19 Italian cathedral (5)
20 Variety show (5)

Across

7 End (6)

8 Sharpening (6)

9 Sharply curved (4)

10 Supplier (8)

11 Hindered (7)

13 Unable to move (5)

15 Put clothes on (5)

16 Largest (7)

18 Sudden heavy rain shower (8)

19 Narrated (4)

21 Did not succeed (6)

22 Part of a song (6)

Down

1 Climbing plant (4)

2 Upsettingly (13)

3 Division of a book (7)

4 Predatory marine fish (5)

5 Act of research (13)

6 Bills (8)

12 Aromatic herb (8)

14 Small mound (7)

17 Overly showy (5)

20 Noisy (4)

CROSSWORD 19

Across

7 Cloth or fabric (8)
8 Oust (anag.) (4)
9 Applaud (4)
10 Remaining; surplus (8)
11 Noting down (7)
12 Smiles radiantly (5)
15 Hit hard (5)
17 Accept to be true (7)
20 Top boat in a fleet (8)
22 Rotate (4)
23 Emperor of Rome 54-68 AD (4)
24 Boldly (8)

Down

1 Pastiness (6)
2 Tyrannical (8)
3 Happy to do something (7)
4 Divided into two (5)
5 Company symbol (4)
6 Body of running water (6)
13 Living (8)
14 Cook in hot fat (4-3)
16 Liquefied (6)
18 Truly (6)
19 Low dull sounds (5)
21 Well-behaved (4)

Across

1 Conflict or struggle (6)
5 Secret agent (3)
7 Viewpoint or angle (5)
8 Best (7)
9 Organ situated in the skull (5)
10 Relating to the heart (8)
12 Furthest; extreme (6)
14 Contemplate (6)
17 War memorial (8)
18 Large bags (5)
20 Small Arctic whale (7)
21 Highways (5)
22 Wily (3)
23 Resistant to something (6)

Down

2 Highest (7)
3 Advocacy of women's rights (8)
4 Baby sheep (4)
5 Cooked over boiling water (7)
6 Less old (7)
7 Clever (5)
11 Flat image that looks 3D (8)
12 Classic James Joyce novel (7)
13 Liquid metallic element (7)
15 Give reasons for (7)
16 People aged 13-19 (5)
19 Petty quarrel (4)

CROSSWORD 21

Across

1 Act of rebuking severely (11)
9 Charming and endearing (5)
10 Material from which a metal is extracted (3)
11 Stem of an arrow (5)
12 Hides (5)
13 Excessive or affected modesty (8)
16 Free from error (8)
18 Extinct birds (5)
21 Piece of furniture (5)
22 Edible nut (3)
23 Less common (5)
24 Pain in a person's belly (7,4)

Down

2 Living in water (7)
3 Challenging (7)
4 Welcomes (6)
5 ___ pole: tribal emblem (5)
6 Double-reed instruments (5)
7 Make in bulk (4-7)
8 Quantification (11)
14 European country (7)
15 Day of rest (7)
17 Religious leader (6)
19 A payment made (5)
20 Go away from quickly (5)

Across

1 Glue (8)

5 Brag about (4)

9 Garden tool for cutting grass (5)

10 Floor of a building (5)

11 Not logical (10)

14 Turbulence (6)

15 The back of the neck (6)

17 The meaning of a word (10)

20 A satellite of Uranus (5)

21 Dog (5)

22 Playthings (4)

23 Makes a high-pitched sound (8)

Down

1 Military force (4)

2 Bird of prey (4)

3 Shockingly (12)

4 Concerned with sight (6)

6 Famished (8)

7 Undomesticated animals (8)

8 Ordinary dress (5,7)

12 A quarter of a circle (8)

13 Cunningly (8)

16 Sew (6)

18 Body of a ship (4)

19 Lyric poems (4)

CROSSWORD 23

Across
1 Counterfeit (5)
4 Alongside each other (7)
7 Fixed platform by water (5)
8 Comical (8)
9 Conflict (5)
11 Settles (8)
15 Part of the brain (8)
17 Put in considerable effort (5)
19 Small turtle (8)
20 Notices (5)
21 Evergreen conifer (7)
22 Woody-stemmed plant (5)

Down
1 Capital of Romania (9)
2 Quick look (7)
3 Soon (7)
4 Renounce an oath (6)
5 Breathe out (6)
6 Rises (anag.) (5)
10 Mouth organ (9)
12 Strangely (7)
13 Puzzling and obscure (7)
14 Superior (6)
16 Votes into office (6)
18 Answer (5)

CROSSWORD 24

Across

1 Wages (8)
5 Smudge (4)
8 Opposite of tall (5)
9 Argues against (7)
10 Fifth Greek letter (7)
12 Country whose capital is Reykjavik (7)
14 Shelf support (7)
16 Public collection of books (7)
18 Active during the day (7)
19 Ethos (anag.) (5)
20 Takes to court (4)
21 Group of symptoms which occur together (8)

Down

1 Simplicity (4)
2 Novice (6)
3 Among other things (Latin) (5,4)
4 Shone (6)
6 Finally (6)
7 Sonorous (8)
11 Parted (9)
12 Incorporates (8)
13 Dull (6)
14 Subsidiary action (6)
15 Japanese dress (6)
17 Where you are (4)

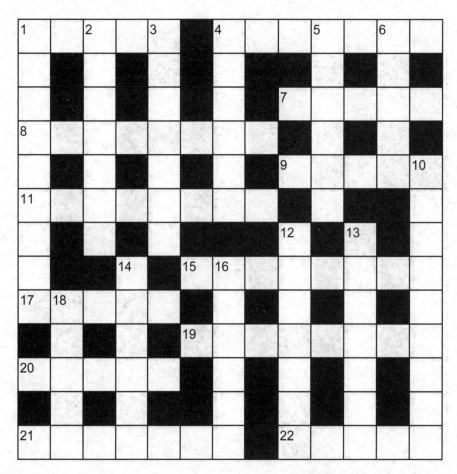

Across

1 Relating to a city (5)

4 Easy shots or catches (in sport) (7)

7 Capital of South Korea (5)

8 Containing less oxygen than usual (of air) (8)

9 Small loose stones (5)

11 E.g. from Montreal (8)

15 Extremely happy (8)

17 Beastly (5)

19 Neat and smart (5-3)

20 Judges; considers to be (5)

21 Unintelligent (7)

22 Very informal phrases (5)

Down

1 Sign of the zodiac (9)

2 Bright and striking (7)

3 Entrust a secret to another (7)

4 Representation of a concept; diagram (6)

5 Deep ditch (6)

6 Awaken (5)

10 Instructing (9)

12 Bundles of grain stalks (7)

13 Windpipe (7)

14 Part of a flower (6)

16 Different from (6)

18 Regions (5)

Across

1 Crafty; cunning (8)
5 Pierce with a knife (4)
9 Obtain information from various sources (5)
10 Sour substances (5)
11 Formal forgiveness (10)
14 Solemn promise (6)
15 Sprints (6)
17 Prove erroneous (10)
20 Plant spike (5)
21 Take delight in (5)
22 Rough or harsh sound (4)
23 Acceptance of something as true (8)

Down

1 Droops (4)
2 Pay close attention to (4)
3 Startling (4-8)
4 Concept (6)
6 Gloaming (8)
7 Commerce (8)
8 Made (12)
12 Sliver of wood (8)
13 Permeable (8)
16 Worshipper (6)
18 Cooking appliance (4)
19 Run away (4)

CROSSWORD 27

Across

1 Respectful (11)
9 Enclosed (of animals) (5)
10 Unwell (3)
11 E.g. incisors and molars (5)
12 Delicious (5)
13 How a crab moves (8)
16 Lasting (8)
18 Heavy iron tool (5)
21 Molten rock (5)
22 Mountain pass (3)
23 South American animal (5)
24 Act quickly (3,8)

Down

2 Increases a deadline (7)
3 Shuns (7)
4 Fourscore (6)
5 This date (5)
6 Self-evident truth (5)
7 Satisfactory (2,2,7)
8 E.g. Queen of Hearts (7,4)
14 European country (7)
15 Coarsen (7)
17 Leaping antelope (6)
19 One-way flow structure (5)
20 Sweet-scented shrub (5)

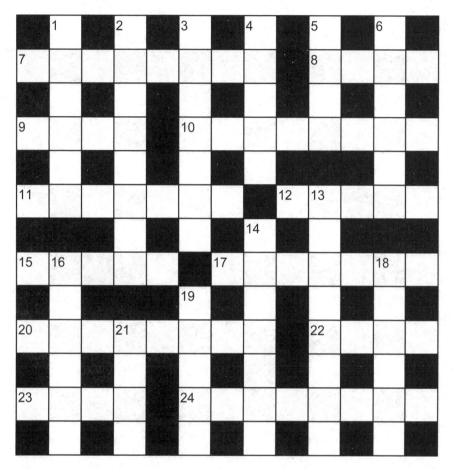

Across

7 Resolution (8)

8 Still to be paid (4)

9 Pulp (4)

10 Deferrer (anag.) (8)

11 Confident (7)

12 Estuary (5)

15 Hit; steal (5)

17 Frees from an obligation (7)

20 Booklet (8)

22 Back of the neck (4)

23 Departs (4)

24 Supported with money (8)

Down

1 Prohibits (6)

2 Athletics event (4,4)

3 Penetrated (7)

4 Breathe in audibly (5)

5 Guided journey (4)

6 One appointed to administer a state (6)

13 Inherent (8)

14 Going out (7)

16 Fighting instrument (6)

18 Knocked gently (6)

19 Light downy particles (5)

21 Small bunch of flowers (4)

CROSSWORD 29

Across

1 The actors in a show (4)
3 Irate spy (anag.) (8)
9 Pig's foot (7)
10 Obnoxiously forward (5)
11 Strikingly (12)
13 Large military unit (6)
15 Penetrate (6)
17 Wearing glasses (12)
20 Moisten meat (5)
21 Discard from memory (7)
22 Sororal (8)
23 Dull heavy sound (4)

Down

1 Strongholds (8)
2 Minute pore in a leaf (5)
4 Narrow passage of water (6)
5 Vehemently (12)
6 Separated; remote (7)
7 Spool-like toy (4)
8 Atmospheric layer (12)
12 Made (a noise) less intense (8)
14 Estimates (7)
16 Real (6)
18 Restraint for an animal (5)
19 Falls back (4)

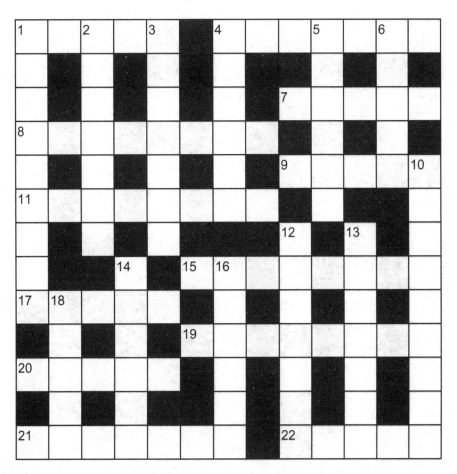

Across

1 Annoyed (5)

4 Block (7)

7 Glasses (abbrev.) (5)

8 Pursuit of high principles (8)

9 Mocks (5)

11 Illnesses (8)

15 Reload (8)

17 Military opponent (5)

19 Self-operating machines (8)

20 Fabric with parallel ribs (5)

21 Ugly building (7)

22 Conceals (5)

Down

1 Not inevitable (9)

2 Antelope (7)

3 Gave way to pressure (7)

4 Compensate for (6)

5 Drank with the tongue (6)

6 The furnishings in a room (5)

10 Love songs (9)

12 From beginning to end (7)

13 Lubricated (7)

14 Walks slowly (6)

16 Agree or correspond (6)

18 Recently (5)

CROSSWORD 31

Across

1 Telescope lens (8)
5 Celebration; festivity (4)
8 Prize (5)
9 Claimed (anag.) (7)
10 Given generously (7)
12 Severely (7)
14 Character in Hamlet (7)
16 Not crying (3-4)
18 Encroachments (7)
19 Therefore (5)
20 Conceal (4)
21 Excited; lively (8)

Down

1 Feeling of strong eagerness (4)
2 Make possible (6)
3 Secure against legal responsibility (9)
4 Huggable (6)
6 Regard with approval (6)
7 Exclamation of joy (8)
11 Birthplace of Jesus (9)
12 Popular lunch food (8)
13 Composite of different species (6)
14 More likely than not (4-2)
15 Small finch (6)
17 Join together by heating with a blowpipe (4)

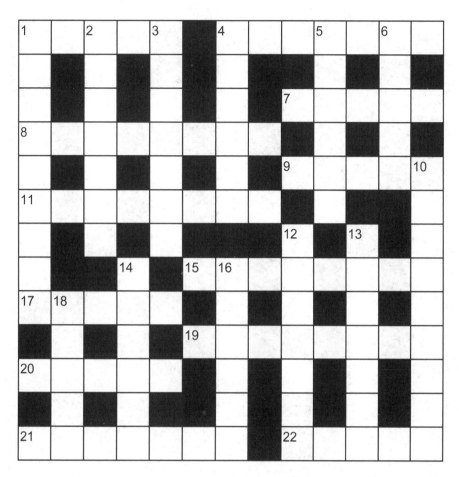

Across

1 Ahead of time (5)
4 Novelty (7)
7 Ring (5)
8 Small pocket tool (8)
9 Impudent (5)
11 Foot soldiers (8)
15 Cartoon artist (8)
17 Personnel at work (5)
19 Capital of Finland (8)
20 Go to see (5)
21 Made available for sale (7)
22 Grain storage chambers (5)

Down

1 E.g. residents of Cairo (9)
2 Reintegrate (7)
3 Expressing boredom with the mouth (7)
4 E.g. Rory McIlroy (6)
5 Pertaining to the mind (6)
6 Prison compartments (5)
10 Desires; longings (9)
12 Breaks (7)
13 Template (7)
14 Workplace (6)
16 Required (6)
18 Robber (5)

CROSSWORD 33

Across

1 Heavy fall of rain (8)
5 Desert in central China (4)
8 Artificial waterway (5)
9 Nonconformist (7)
10 Raises dough (using yeast) (7)
12 Snatched (7)
14 Liberate; release (7)
16 Type of monkey (7)
18 Refills (7)
19 Shallow circular dish (5)
20 Painful (4)
21 Utopian (8)

Down

1 Waterbird with webbed feet (4)
2 ___ Ryder: US actress (6)
3 Large white arctic animal (5,4)
4 Maintain a decision (6)
6 Vent (6)
7 Cut (8)
11 Non-canonical religious texts (9)
12 Body movements that convey meaning (8)
13 Marble (anag.) (6)
14 In mint condition (6)
15 Opposite of an acid (6)
17 Plant with an edible root (4)

Across

7 Send to a different place (8)
8 Tardy (4)
9 Couple (4)
10 People who repair pipes and fittings (8)
11 Mournful poems (7)
12 Breezy (5)
15 Rotates (5)
17 Artificial (3-4)
20 Freshwater crustacean (8)
22 Tip the hat (4)
23 Fish (4)
24 Awkwardly (8)

Down

1 Nitty-gritty (6)
2 Atmospheric gas (8)
3 Places of worship (7)
4 Play a guitar (5)
5 Fluent but shallow (of words) (4)
6 Gazed (6)
13 Shameless (8)
14 Timid (7)
16 Chase (6)
18 Dexterously (6)
19 An easy task (5)
21 Chinese monetary unit (4)

CROSSWORD 35

Across

1 Soft pear-shaped fruits (4)
3 Loud and harsh (8)
9 Procedure; standard (7)
10 In a slow tempo (of music) (5)
11 Poorly fed (12)
14 Male aristocrat (3)
16 Senior figure in a tribe (5)
17 Hill (3)
18 Able to use both hands well (12)
21 Large mast (5)
22 Uncomplaining (7)
23 Trapped in a small space (8)
24 Spheres (4)

Down

1 First in importance (8)
2 Type of porridge (5)
4 Foot extremity (3)
5 Picture (12)
6 Serious and sincere (7)
7 Run at moderate pace (4)
8 Insubordination (12)
12 Natural elevation (5)
13 Stiff coarse hairs (8)
15 Walker without a fixed route (7)
19 Take place; happen (5)
20 Long narrative poem (4)
22 Female pronoun (3)

Across

1 Schemes (5)
4 Act of touching (7)
7 Marrying man (5)
8 Hostilities (8)
9 Deducts (5)
11 Diminished (8)
15 Burning (8)
17 Make a search (5)
19 Unskilled; amateur (8)
20 Metal pieces used as money (5)
21 Protective location (7)
22 Work hard (5)

Down

1 Helpless (9)
2 Furthest away (7)
3 Emit spitting sounds (7)
4 Dairy product (6)
5 Great fear (6)
6 Wedge placed against a wheel (5)
10 Tiniest (9)
12 Tensing a muscle (7)
13 Difficult choice (7)
14 Passageway through rock (6)
16 Bestow (6)
18 Fabric (5)

Across

1 Male hairdresser (6)
7 Introduced fluid into (the body) (8)
8 Sewn edge (3)
9 Pertaining to life (6)
10 Bone of the forearm (4)
11 Workers (5)
13 Drawers (anag.) (7)
15 Adhesive label (7)
17 Uses a keyboard (5)
21 Scottish singer-songwriter (4)
22 Less quiet (6)
23 Unit of current (3)
24 Higher in rank (8)
25 Harsh (6)

Down

1 Opposite of in front (6)
2 Wander without a route (6)
3 Fissures (5)
4 Driven out (7)
5 Precision (8)
6 Inclined at an angle (6)
12 Hermits (8)
14 Speak rhetorically (7)
16 The Bull (starsign) (6)
18 Procession (6)
19 Easy to understand (6)
20 Contented cat sounds (5)

Across

1 Car pedal (11)
9 Pointed part of a fork (5)
10 The gist of the matter (3)
11 Group of shots (5)
12 Prod with the elbow (5)
13 A lament (8)
16 A Roman emperor (8)
18 Knocks into (5)
21 Major African river (5)
22 Popular edible fish (3)
23 Rocky; harsh (5)
24 Accredited diplomats (11)

Down

2 E.g. knives and forks (7)
3 Explain in detail (7)
4 Wore away gradually (6)
5 Inert gas (5)
6 Possessed (5)
7 Transfer responsibility elsewhere (4,3,4)
8 Room used by astronomers (11)
14 Squeezed the skin tightly (7)
15 More amusing (7)
17 Collections of photos (6)
19 Device used to connect to the internet (5)
20 Country in the Middle East (5)

CROSSWORD 39

Across

1 Sentimentality (4)
3 Offer of marriage (8)
9 Exceptionally good (7)
10 Positions in a hierarchy (5)
11 Intended to attract notice (12)
13 Send for sale overseas (6)
15 Point where two edges meet (6)
17 Unfriendly (12)
20 Pull out a hair (5)
21 Devoted time to learning (7)
22 The decade from 1990 - 1999 (8)
23 Coheres; semisolid substances (4)

Down

1 Inaccurate name (8)
2 Perfume (5)
4 Refill (6)
5 Penny-pinching (12)
6 Reddening of the skin (7)
7 One of the seven deadly sins (4)
8 Evening dress for men (6,6)
12 Goes before (8)
14 Flightless seabird (7)
16 Whipped cream dessert (6)
18 Hackneyed (5)
19 Total spread of a bridge (4)

Across

1 Make valid retrospectively (8)
5 Look at amorously (4)
9 Gardeners sow these (5)
10 Not together (5)
11 Puzzlement (10)
14 Exit; Bible book (6)
15 Request earnestly (6)
17 Violation of a law (10)
20 Fishing net (5)
21 Item won in a competition (5)
22 Method of learning by repetition (4)
23 Keep at a distance (8)

Down

1 Greatest (4)
2 Crush or grind food with the teeth (4)
3 Discreditable (12)
4 Boredom (6)
6 Thankful (8)
7 Qualified for by right (8)
8 Person who listens into conversations (12)
12 Official list of names (8)
13 Puffed out (of hair) (8)
16 Long sticks; supplies with personnel (6)
18 Furnace (4)
19 Unit of heredity (4)

CROSSWORD 41

Across

1 Partly open (4)

3 Bright red fruits (8)

9 Longed for (7)

10 Pertaining to bees (5)

11 Written in pictorial symbols (12)

13 Meal (6)

15 Tool used to hit things (6)

17 Aversion to change (12)

20 Stood up (5)

21 Prescribe (7)

22 A formal exposition (8)

23 Proofreader's mark meaning 'let it stand' (4)

Down

1 Not in a specific location (8)

2 Decrease; lessen (5)

4 Nestle together (6)

5 Re-emergence (12)

6 Metal similar to platinum (7)

7 Snag (anag.) (4)

8 Not staying the same throughout (12)

12 Percussion sound (8)

14 Market a product (7)

16 Wears away (6)

18 Not suitable (5)

19 Speak in a wild way (4)

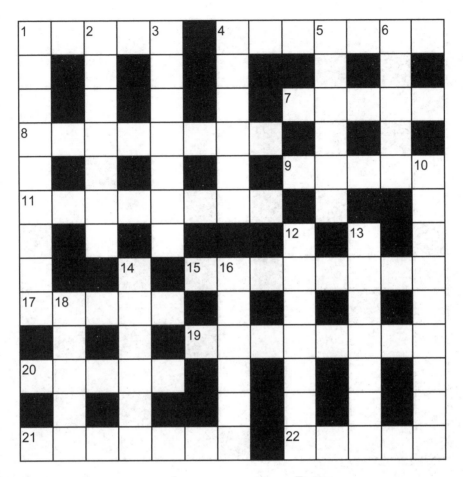

Across

1 Physical strength (5)
4 Spiders spin these (7)
7 Sailing boat (5)
8 Murmured (8)
9 Small cluster (5)
11 Legible (8)
15 Natural liking for (8)
17 Sticky (5)
19 Written laws (8)
20 Puff on a cigarette (5)
21 Breathing aid in water (7)
22 Relay (anag.) (5)

Down

1 Curved piece of wood (9)
2 Coming from the south (7)
3 Digit (7)
4 Breakfast food (6)
5 Crazily (6)
6 Plant flower (5)
10 Synthetic fabric (9)
12 Plaited lock of hair (7)
13 Relating to what one eats (7)
14 Quidditch position in Harry Potter (6)
16 Recurring irregularly (6)
18 Yellow citrus fruit (5)

Across

1 Small body of rainwater (6)
4 What a spider makes (6)
9 Exhaling audibly (7)
10 Innocently (7)
11 Big cats (5)
12 Instruct; teach (5)
14 Show pleasure facially (5)
15 Worthiness (5)
17 Male bee (5)
18 Fear of heights (7)
20 Offence (7)
21 Fatty matter (6)
22 East (6)

Down

1 Grinding tool (6)
2 Well-meaning but interfering person (2-6)
3 Dens (5)
5 Remove a difficulty (7)
6 Broad (4)
7 Subatomic particle such as a nucleon (6)
8 Humiliating (11)
13 Assign (8)
14 Walks with long steps (7)
15 Affecting the emotions (6)
16 Of the immediate past (6)
17 Prohibit (5)
19 Thick cord (4)

Across

7 Dedicate (6)

8 Entirely (6)

9 Lose one's footing (4)

10 Containing many inhabitants (8)

11 Release (7)

13 Lukewarm (5)

15 Weeps (5)

16 Strong reaction of anger (7)

18 Breaking suddenly and violently (8)

19 Fling (4)

21 Reveal (anag.) (6)

22 Sport Serena Williams plays (6)

Down

1 Examine by touch (4)

2 Wide-ranging (13)

3 Storm (7)

4 Exchanges (5)

5 Deep consideration of oneself (4-9)

6 Making less clear (8)

12 Protects and cares for (8)

14 Spending funds (7)

17 Levels; ranks (5)

20 Attack at speed (4)

CROSSWORD 45

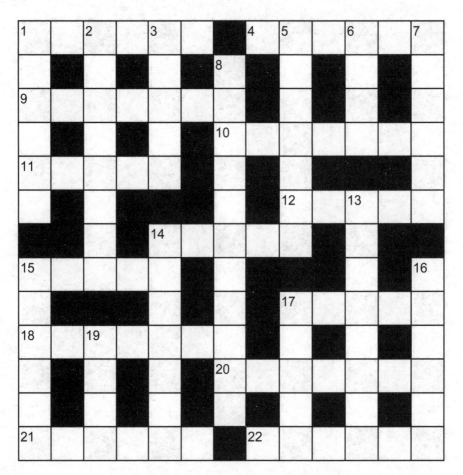

Across

1 Paths of electrons around nuclei (6)
4 Distorts (6)
9 Jovially celebratory (7)
10 Hammers (7)
11 Tumbles (5)
12 Fortunate (5)
14 Cover with liquid (5)
15 Embarrass (5)
17 Small cabin (5)
18 Shine like a star (7)
20 Becomes less wide (7)
21 Creative act (6)
22 Large strong boxes (6)

Down

1 Makes available for sale (6)
2 Roman building (8)
3 Two children born at the same time (5)
5 Earthly (7)
6 Unspecified in number (4)
7 Sloppy (6)
8 Character; nature (11)
13 Warns (8)
14 Trembling (7)
15 Be present at (6)
16 Pursues (6)
17 Cruel or severe (5)
19 Part of the eye (4)

Across

1 Depletion of water from the body (11)
9 Tawdry (5)
10 Female deer (3)
11 Employer (5)
12 Monotonous hum (5)
13 Marriage ceremony (8)
16 Reproduce (8)
18 Scores an exam paper (5)
21 Concerning (5)
22 Zero (3)
23 Lazed (5)
24 Youth (11)

Down

2 Encode (7)
3 Chemical element with symbol Y (7)
4 Part of the eye (6)
5 Secret rendezvous (5)
6 More mature (5)
7 Accomplishment (11)
8 Opposite of temporarily (11)
14 Foot pedal (7)
15 Terse (7)
17 Large birds of prey (6)
19 Governed (5)
20 Ability; talent (5)

CROSSWORD 47

Across

1 Team (4)
3 Straw hat (8)
9 Took away (7)
10 Lines (anag.) (5)
11 Perceptions (12)
14 Take or steal something (3)
16 Nearby (5)
17 Cheek (slang) (3)
18 Unseen observer (3,2,3,4)
21 Assesses performance (5)
22 Boxing up (7)
23 Showering with liquid (8)
24 Leg joint (4)

Down

1 Overcome a difficulty (8)
2 Ditches (5)
4 Eccentric (3)
5 Hostility (12)
6 Endless (7)
7 Expel; drive out (4)
8 In a greedy manner (12)
12 Select; choose (5)
13 Concluding section (8)
15 Support (7)
19 Negatively charged ion (5)
20 Makes a mistake (4)
22 Animal enclosure (3)

Across

1 Of a court of law (8)
5 Moved through water (4)
9 Place of refuge (5)
10 Bitterly pungent (5)
11 File linked to an email (10)
14 Not allowing light to pass through (6)
15 Quantity (6)
17 Destroy (10)
20 Sully or blemish (5)
21 Conceal (5)
22 Garden outbuilding (4)
23 Stated emphatically (8)

Down

1 Fourth Gospel (4)
2 Prima donna (4)
3 Building (12)
4 Breathing passage (6)
6 Excessively emotional (6,2)
7 Think deeply for a period of time (8)
8 Relating to numbers (12)
12 Gigantic statue (8)
13 E.g. rugby or tennis (4,4)
16 Treat without seriousness (6)
18 Finished; complete (4)
19 Network of lines (4)

CROSSWORD 49

Across

1 Claw (6)
5 Make a sound quieter (6)
8 Puns (anag.) (4)
9 Representative example (8)
10 Disregard the rules (5)
11 Believe tentatively (7)
14 An event with good and bad implications (5,8)
16 Capital of China (7)
18 Mammals with bushy tails (5)
20 Corrosive precipitation (4,4)
22 Head coverings (4)
23 Not present (6)
24 Planetary bodies (6)

Down

2 Spontaneous (9)
3 Befuddle (7)
4 Ready to eat (of fruit) (4)
5 Raider (8)
6 Frustrated and annoyed (3,2)
7 Piece of wood (3)
12 Blocked up; crowded (9)
13 Very plentiful (8)
15 Suppress a feeling (7)
17 Arbiter (5)
19 Was aware of; understood (4)
21 Taxi (3)

Across

7 Lofty peak (8)

8 Preparation for Easter (4)

9 Silent (4)

10 Daydreamer (8)

11 Stammer (7)

12 Person acting as a deputy (5)

15 Reject with disdain (5)

17 Drop sharply (7)

20 Microorganisms (8)

22 Bites at (4)

23 Boring (4)

24 Good manners (8)

Down

1 French dance (6)

2 Mammal with a sticky tongue (8)

3 Planned one's actions (7)

4 Area of sand (5)

5 Flutter (4)

6 For men and women (of clothing) (6)

13 Chew cud (8)

14 Tidy (5,2)

16 Ornamental tablet fixed to a wall (6)

18 Show up; reveal (6)

19 Elegance; class (5)

21 Lite (anag.) (4)

Across

1 Small mammals resembling mice (6)
5 Increase the running speed of an engine (3)
7 Closely compacted (5)
8 Beat easily (7)
9 Position carefully (5)
10 E.g. plaice (8)
12 Dribbles (6)
14 Talks excessively about one's talents (6)
17 20th-century art movement (8)
18 Red-chested bird (5)
20 Crush underfoot (7)
21 Hidden storage space (5)
22 Long-haired ox (3)
23 Deactivate an explosive device (6)

Down

2 Jumping athlete (7)
3 Unexpected gain (8)
4 Cut (4)
5 Actress (anag.) (7)
6 Coatings (7)
7 Believer in a supreme being (5)
11 Fill (with data) (8)
12 Opening to a room (7)
13 Remote districts of Australia (7)
15 Scuffles (7)
16 Cite (5)
19 Pleasant (4)

Across

1 Strongbox (4)
3 Attributing to (8)
9 Canvas shelters (7)
10 Darken (5)
11 Most prominent position (5,2,5)
14 Loud noise (3)
16 Select class (5)
17 Depression (3)
18 Birds of prey (6,6)
21 Large intestine (5)
22 Capital of the US state of Georgia (7)
23 Sweet food courses (8)
24 Give up one's rights (4)

Down

1 Rush of animals (8)
2 Spore-producing organisms (5)
4 Title of a married woman (3)
5 Hard to fathom (12)
6 Brought about (7)
7 Willing to do something (4)
8 Freedom from control (12)
12 Pretend (5)
13 Religious deserter (8)
15 Pasta strips (7)
19 Sudden movement (5)
20 Corrosive substance (4)
22 Small social insect (3)

CROSSWORD 53

Across

1 Least quiet (8)
5 Familiar name for a potato (4)
9 Suit (5)
10 Groups of animals (5)
11 Intelligence (10)
14 Humorously sarcastic (6)
15 Time of widespread glaciation (3,3)
17 A detail (10)
20 Spin quickly (5)
21 A clearing in a wood (5)
22 Opposite of low (4)
23 Official orders (8)

Down

1 Pen points (4)
2 Doubtful (4)
3 Comprehensible (12)
4 Deviate suddenly (6)
6 Italian cheese (8)
7 Catastrophe (8)
8 Cheated someone financially (5-7)
12 Send off to a destination (8)
13 Getting onto a ship (8)
16 Domed roof (6)
18 Small pointed missile (4)
19 Allows to happen (4)

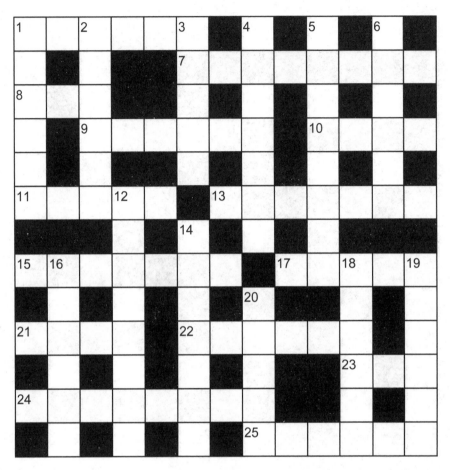

Across

1 Nearly (6)

7 Viewers (8)

8 Male person (3)

9 High-kicking dance (6)

10 Raise (4)

11 Strong currents of air (5)

13 Extremely bad (7)

15 Opposes (7)

17 Baked sweet treats (5)

21 Burst or break (4)

22 Without affection (6)

23 Short cylindrical piece of wood (3)

24 Felony (8)

25 Abrupt (6)

Down

1 Intending (6)

2 Cuts up meat very finely (6)

3 Two times (5)

4 Substitute (7)

5 Personal magnetism (8)

6 Printed mistakes (6)

12 Decade from 1920 - 1929 (8)

14 Equipped (7)

16 Purchased (6)

18 Data input device (6)

19 Catchphrase (6)

20 Engages in a game (5)

CROSSWORD 55

Across

1 Overseas (6)
4 Book of the Bible (6)
9 US space probe to Jupiter (7)
10 Sanction (7)
11 Make good on a debt (5)
12 Unconditional love (5)
14 Pleasantly warm (of weather) (5)
15 Entrance hallway (5)
17 Reside (5)
18 Kettledrums (7)
20 Eight-sided shape (7)
21 Not masculine or feminine (6)
22 Doglike mammals (6)

Down

1 Annoys (6)
2 The acting out of a particular part (4,4)
3 Narrow passageway (5)
5 Surface where ships are built (7)
6 Ring of light around the head (4)
7 Go back on a promise (6)
8 Process of clotting; curdling (11)
13 Substance causing a reaction (8)
14 Respire (7)
15 Plump up (6)
16 Catapults (6)
17 Short simple song (5)
19 List of food items available (4)

Across

1 Happy (6)
5 Eastern temple (6)
8 Writing fluids (4)
9 Cautions (8)
10 Sound made by a frog (5)
11 Not tidy (7)
14 Incapable of being expressed in words (13)
16 Tomato sauce (7)
18 Feeling pleased and satisfied (5)
20 Agitated (8)
22 Legume (4)
23 For the time being (3,3)
24 Sailing vessels (6)

Down

2 Impediment (9)
3 Entrap (7)
4 Open the mouth wide when tired (4)
5 Unreasonably anxious about (8)
6 Dirt (5)
7 Excavate (3)
12 Contaminant (9)
13 Make used to (8)
15 Type of respiration (7)
17 Where tennis is played (5)
19 Wear away (4)
21 Evergreen coniferous tree (3)

CROSSWORD 57

Across

1 Tossing and catching items continuously (8)
5 Speech impediment (4)
8 Burrowing animals (5)
9 Master of ceremonies (7)
10 Alternative forms of genes (7)
12 Mythical being (7)
14 Evaluating competition entries (7)
16 Inactive pill (7)
18 Think deeply about (7)
19 Consent to (5)
20 Aromatic herb (4)
21 Turns around (8)

Down

1 Leap (4)
2 Measure of capacity (6)
3 Hopeless situation (4,5)
4 Sugary flower secretion (6)
6 Standards of perfection (6)
7 Agreeable (8)
11 Painting that depicts scenery (9)
12 Contrasted (8)
13 Legitimate (6)
14 Bump against roughly (6)
15 Accustoms to something (6)
17 Streams of liquid or gas (4)

Across

1 Religious group (4)
3 Pepper plant (8)
9 Ways of doing things (7)
10 Finished (5)
11 Container for a drink (3)
12 Person who flies an aircraft (5)
13 Relative by marriage (2-3)
15 Absorbent cloth (5)
17 Bend (5)
18 Popular beverage (3)
19 Not concealed (5)
20 Junction between nerve cells (7)
21 Reading carefully (8)
22 Examine quickly (4)

Down

1 Partially awake (13)
2 Destroy (3,2)
4 Descend down a rock face (6)
5 Somnambulism (12)
6 Mark written under a letter (7)
7 Large sea (13)
8 Constantly; always (12)
14 Upstart; one who has recently gained wealth (7)
16 Grow more ill (6)
18 Theme for a discussion (5)

Across

1 Court enclosure (4)

3 Amended (8)

9 Reinstate (7)

10 Short-tempered; ardent (5)

11 Separately (12)

14 Conciliatory gift (3)

16 Bolt for fastening metal plates (5)

17 Health resort (3)

18 Productive insight (12)

21 Small antelope (5)

22 Distances (7)

23 Saltiness (8)

24 A group of three (4)

Down

1 Least clean (8)

2 Enclosed (5)

4 Owed and payable (3)

5 Uncomplimentary (12)

6 Lattice (7)

7 24 hour periods (4)

8 Discussion (12)

12 Quilt (5)

13 Exaggerated masculinity (8)

15 Incomplete (7)

19 Speak; total (5)

20 Tiny specks (4)

22 Allow (3)

Across

1 Devices that tell the time (6)

7 Fictitious (8)

8 Wager (3)

9 Case for holding money (6)

10 Fall slowly (of water) (4)

11 Tiny arachnids (5)

13 Cunning (7)

15 Flee (7)

17 Work tables (5)

21 Express a desire for (4)

22 Speaker (6)

23 Put a question to (3)

24 Justified in terms of profitability (8)

25 Small hills (6)

Down

1 Style and movement in art (6)

2 Deceive with ingenuity (6)

3 One of the senses (5)

4 Majestic (7)

5 Trachea (8)

6 Starve with hunger (6)

12 Grounding (of electricity) (8)

14 Hour of going to sleep (7)

16 Settle decisively (6)

18 Bad handwriting (6)

19 Limbless reptiles (6)

20 Become suddenly understandable (5)

Across

1 Responds to (6)
5 Peevish and annoyed (6)
8 Luxurious car (abbrev.) (4)
9 Specific place or area (8)
10 Of sedate character (5)
11 Remaining (7)
14 Unbelievably (13)
16 Scorn (7)
18 Fabric used to make jeans (5)
20 Explosive (8)
22 Among (4)
23 Uttered (6)
24 Spirited horses (6)

Down

2 Being (9)
3 Spicy Spanish sausage (7)
4 E.g. auction (4)
5 Alcoholic drink with several ingredients (8)
6 Alleviate (5)
7 Mouthpiece attached to a bridle (3)
12 Invalidated (9)
13 A division between people (8)
15 Mediocre (7)
17 Silly trick (5)
19 Animals kept at home (4)
21 Pay (anag.) (3)

CROSSWORD 62

Across

1 Urban area (4)
3 Respondent (8)
9 Agitated (7)
10 Egg-shaped (5)
11 Accomplishments (12)
13 Hinder (6)
15 Sewing instrument (6)
17 Author of screenplays (12)
20 Firearm (5)
21 Chief officer (7)
22 Rump (8)
23 Tax (4)

Down

1 State of Australia (8)
2 Measure heaviness (5)
4 Pokes gently (6)
5 Showing complete commitment (12)
6 Cooked meat in the oven (7)
7 Roll of photographic film (4)
8 Amiability (12)
12 Privately (8)
14 Large ocean (7)
16 Unintelligent (6)
18 Sheet (anag.) (5)
19 Insect larva (4)

CROSSWORD 63

Across

7 Hidden store of valuables (8,5)
8 Fraudster (8)
9 Distort (4)
10 Boxes (7)
12 Bundle of wheat (5)
14 Sport played with an oval ball (5)
16 Pledge (7)
19 Bend (4)
20 Stubbornness (8)
22 Unplanned (13)

Down

1 Hilltop (4)
2 Is unable to (6)
3 Opposite of pushing (7)
4 Ales (5)
5 Process of increasing in size (6)
6 Bridge above another road (8)
11 Like an eagle (8)
13 Acknowledgements (7)
15 Fist fighting (6)
17 The next day (6)
18 Celestial body (5)
21 Persuade gently (4)

Across

1 A single time (4)
3 Partially hidden (8)
9 Spruce up (7)
10 Tortilla topped with cheese (5)
11 Donation (12)
13 Address a person boldly (6)
15 Basic metrical unit in a poem (6)
17 Ineptness (12)
20 Turf out (5)
21 Sign of the zodiac (7)
22 Starlike symbol (8)
23 Walk with heavy steps (4)

Down

1 Public and formal (8)
2 Remove dirt (5)
4 Pygmy chimpanzee (6)
5 Person's physical state (12)
6 Nocturnal carnivorous mammal (7)
7 Pairs of people (4)
8 Marksman (12)
12 Infancy (8)
14 Be made of (7)
16 Musical works (6)
18 Country in the Himalayas (5)
19 Second Greek letter (4)

CROSSWORD 65

Across

1 Large solitary cats (6)
4 Type of music (3-3)
9 River of South East Africa (7)
10 Totally (7)
11 Mashes (5)
12 Weary (5)
14 Strain (5)
15 Strength (5)
17 Erodes (5)
18 Decide firmly (7)
20 Style of cooking (7)
21 Food that is not liquid (6)
22 Altitude (6)

Down

1 Spring flowers (6)
2 Betting (8)
3 Chambers (5)
5 Install; establish (7)
6 Listen to (4)
7 Took part in a game (6)
8 Verify again (6-5)
13 Narrating (8)
14 Stiff and unnatural (7)
15 Bog (6)
16 Upward slope (6)
17 During (5)
19 Earth (4)

Across

1 Large group of fish (6)
5 Long bench (3)
7 Small crude shelter (5)
8 Painting medium (7)
9 Person who eats in a restaurant (5)
10 Value greatly (8)
12 Sharp cutting implements (6)
14 Ranked based on merit (6)
17 Imitative work (8)
18 Totally erases (5)
20 Dignified conduct (7)
21 Views; observes (5)
22 A man; fellow (3)
23 Doles out (6)

Down

2 V-shaped mark (7)
3 Go beyond a limit (8)
4 Roman poet (4)
5 Put in the ground (7)
6 Grew tired (7)
7 Hazardous or difficult (5)
11 Etiquette (8)
12 Done in full awareness (7)
13 Clumsily (7)
15 Wear out completely (7)
16 Groups of musicians (5)
19 Frozen precipitation (4)

CROSSWORD 67

Across

1 Remedial (8)
5 Musical composition (4)
8 Foot-operated lever (5)
9 Biting sharply (7)
10 Omission of a sound when speaking (7)
12 If (7)
14 Antiquated (7)
16 Goals (7)
18 Say again (7)
19 Natural yellow resin (5)
20 Soft drink (US) (4)
21 Elastic (8)

Down

1 Drinking vessels (4)
2 Poser; enigma (6)
3 Call (9)
4 Coating (6)
6 Starting point (6)
7 Very large (8)
11 Vaccinate (9)
12 Cowboy films (8)
13 Deleted (6)
14 Feature (6)
15 Middle Eastern language (6)
17 Hunted animal (4)

Across

1 Packs of cards (5)
4 E.g. Swan Lake and The Nutcracker (7)
7 Watched secretly (5)
8 Venerated (8)
9 Birds that are a symbol of peace (5)
11 Many (8)
15 Last (8)
17 Domestic cat (5)
19 Not forward (8)
20 Parody (5)
21 Ruled (7)
22 Awards (informal) (5)

Down

1 Fraudulent (9)
2 Unit of electric charge (7)
3 Temporary stay (7)
4 Writing desk (6)
5 Portable computer (6)
6 Subject of a talk (5)
10 Machines that cut up paper (9)
12 Joining together (7)
13 Model of excellence (7)
14 Elongated rectangle (6)
16 Jumped in the air (6)
18 Fruit (5)

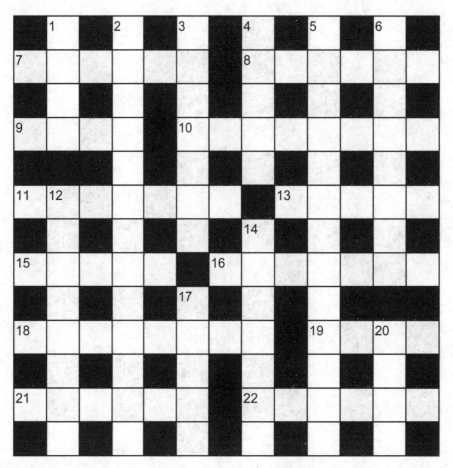

Across

7 Trigonometric function (6)
8 Graphical representation of a person (6)
9 Departed (4)
10 A tiny portion of matter (8)
11 No pears (anag.) (7)
13 Distorts (5)
15 Creates (5)
16 Navigational instrument (7)
18 Imitate (8)
19 Undergarment (4)
21 Shouted out (6)
22 Recently (6)

Down

1 E.g. femur or humerus (4)
2 Repugnantly (13)
3 E.g. swords and guns (7)
4 Unite in matrimony (5)
5 Property of elements with unstable nuclei (13)
6 Become chaotic and out of control (8)
12 Looked at in detail (8)
14 Revokes (7)
17 Curved outwards (of a person's legs) (5)
20 Fine soft thread (4)

Across

1 Energetically or vigorously (11)
9 Tiny piece of food (5)
10 Bitumen (3)
11 Extent (5)
12 Swift (5)
13 Unnecessary concern with minutiae (8)
16 Thick drink (8)
18 Valleys (5)
21 Calls out loudly (5)
22 At this moment (3)
23 Follows orders (5)
24 Occurring at the same time (11)

Down

2 Camera stands (7)
3 Bewitch (7)
4 Loan shark (6)
5 Brown earth pigment (5)
6 Abatement (5)
7 Free from control (11)
8 One who held a job previously (11)
14 Become husky (7)
15 Massage technique (7)
17 Extraterrestrial rock (6)
19 Humble (5)
20 Indifferent to emotions (5)

Across

1 Place with temporary accommodation (4)

3 Foretells (8)

9 Goes back on a promise (7)

10 Stringed instrument (5)

11 Don (anag.) (3)

12 Climb onto (5)

13 Appeal (5)

15 Entices (5)

17 Very tall mythical creature (5)

18 Bristle-like appendage (3)

19 Group of singers (5)

20 Do away with (7)

21 Genteel and feminine in manner (8)

22 Ooze (4)

Down

1 Arranged in temporal order (13)

2 Excavated (5)

4 World's largest country (6)

5 Withdraw from service (12)

6 Customs of a society (7)

7 Fairness in following the rules (13)

8 Relating to farming (12)

14 Very hard form of carbon (7)

16 Comment (6)

18 Similar (5)

Across

7 Central parts of cells (6)

8 Award (6)

9 Dam (4)

10 Good-looking (8)

11 Hygienically (7)

13 Hollow metal objects that ring (5)

15 Established custom (5)

16 See (7)

18 Indirect reference (8)

19 Become weary (4)

21 Unemotional (6)

22 Overflows with water (6)

Down

1 Dominion (4)

2 Teasingly (13)

3 Justly (7)

4 Large pebble (5)

5 Dismay and amazement (13)

6 State of total disorder (8)

12 Pamphlets (8)

14 Make something seem worthy (7)

17 Makes fast with ropes (5)

20 Fishing sticks (4)

CROSSWORD 73

Across

1 Peel (4)
3 Capable of being used (8)
9 Small hardy range horse (7)
10 Shoe ties (5)
11 Intentionally (12)
14 Decline (3)
16 Greeting (5)
17 Antelope (3)
18 Forerunners (12)
21 Porcelain (5)
22 Breathed in sharply (7)
23 Implies (8)
24 Fail to speak clearly (4)

Down

1 Curative medicines (8)
2 Of the nose (5)
4 Breed of dog (3)
5 Connection or association (12)
6 Accumulation of uncompleted work (7)
7 Far from difficult (4)
8 Major type of food nutrient (12)
12 Ancient object (5)
13 Person not accepted by society (8)
15 On fire (7)
19 Bits of meat of low value (5)
20 Performs on stage (4)
22 Took an exam (3)

Across

7 Part of a dress (6)

8 Make less tight (6)

9 Liquefy (4)

10 E.g. hats and helmets (8)

11 Handbooks (7)

13 Renown (5)

15 Footwear without heels (5)

16 Aquatic creature with prominent barbels (7)

18 Piece of printed matter (8)

19 Religious act (4)

21 Regnal (anag.) (6)

22 Servile (6)

Down

1 Fruit of the pine (4)

2 Suspiciously (13)

3 Type of precision surgery (7)

4 Outer garment (5)

5 Having patience despite troubles (4-9)

6 Ten-sided shapes (8)

12 In every respect (3-5)

14 Period between sunrise and sunset (7)

17 Boat (5)

20 Set of players (4)

CROSSWORD 75

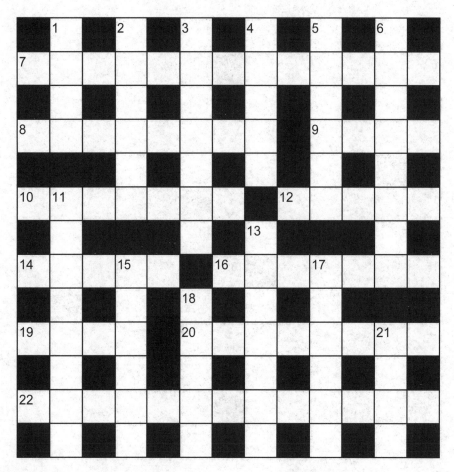

Across

7 Corresponding (13)

8 Solid with straight sides and a circular section (8)

9 Overly submissive (4)

10 Wrangled over price (7)

12 Utter elation (5)

14 Spherical body (5)

16 Flowers (7)

19 Child's bed (4)

20 Small streams (8)

22 Unqualified (13)

Down

1 Salver (4)

2 Season (6)

3 Curbs (7)

4 Platforms leading out to sea (5)

5 Hard tooth coating (6)

6 Accented (8)

11 Enticing (8)

13 Seriousness (7)

15 Large terrestrial monkey (6)

17 Insincere (6)

18 Group of lions (5)

21 Type of wood (4)

Across

1 Weight (4)
3 Mobster (8)
9 Last longer than others (of clothes) (7)
10 Equipped (5)
11 Not capable of justification (12)
13 Song of devotion (6)
15 Heavy load (6)
17 Uncertain (12)
20 Produce a literary work (5)
21 Player of an instrument that is low in pitch (7)
22 Large game bird (8)
23 Inheritor (4)

Down

1 Young ruffian (8)
2 Stinky (5)
4 Exposing one's views (6)
5 Courtesy (12)
6 Fell over (7)
7 Travel by horse (4)
8 Altruism (12)
12 Person who puts money into something (8)
14 Like a bull (7)
16 Decorative strip of fabric (6)
18 Seawater (5)
19 Exchange (4)

Across

1 Unoccupied areas (6)

5 Develop (6)

8 Look or manner (4)

9 In spite of the fact (8)

10 Eat quickly (5)

11 Of the United Kingdom (7)

14 Understandable (13)

16 Retirement income (7)

18 Manipulate dough (5)

20 Put more in a container than it can hold (8)

22 State of the USA (4)

23 Soaks in liquid (6)

24 Quantity of medicine to take (6)

Down

2 Fundamental truth (9)

3 Needle-leaved tree (7)

4 Shut with force (4)

5 Indefatigable (8)

6 Foremost part of anything (5)

7 Fall behind (3)

12 Rescuing from loss (9)

13 Suppositions (8)

15 Having solidified from lava (of rock) (7)

17 Tennis stroke (5)

19 Lids (anag.) (4)

21 Animal doctor (3)

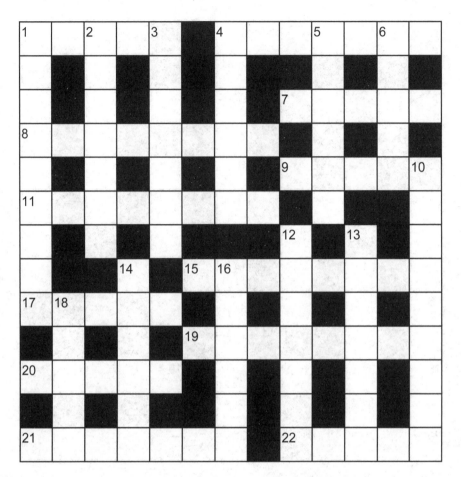

Across

1 Gave away (5)

4 Tries hard (7)

7 Stylishness and originality (5)

8 Frightening (8)

9 Rocks back and forth (5)

11 Living alone (8)

15 Happened (8)

17 Bond or connection (5)

19 Opera texts (8)

20 Crucial person or point (5)

21 Large tracts of land (7)

22 First Pope (5)

Down

1 Artisan (9)

2 Very long lasting (7)

3 Degree of compactness (7)

4 Boil gently (6)

5 Relations by marriage (2-4)

6 Enlighten; educate (5)

10 Wading bird (9)

12 Do something more quickly (5,2)

13 Object strongly (7)

14 Atmospheric phenomenon (6)

16 Holds on tightly (6)

18 Gives out (5)

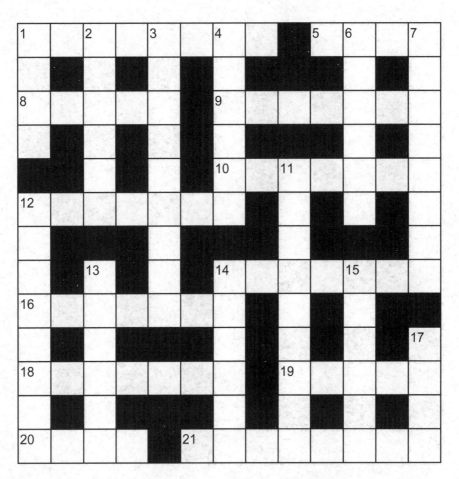

Across

1 Fine soft wool (8)

5 Crush with a sharp blow (4)

8 Pallid (5)

9 Powdered spice (7)

10 Dolorous (7)

12 Person on the staff of an ambassador (7)

14 Accrued (7)

16 Provoked; encouraged (7)

18 Tallier (anag.) (7)

19 West Indian dance (5)

20 Fat used to make puddings (4)

21 Of many different kinds (8)

Down

1 Loose hood (4)

2 Group of six (6)

3 Beggar (9)

4 Hold in high esteem (6)

6 Smells (6)

7 Country in South East Asia (8)

11 Nocturnal insect-eating mammal (9)

12 Greek hero of the Trojan War (8)

13 Hay-cutting tool (6)

14 Grown-ups (6)

15 Surrender (6)

17 Strong link (4)

Across

1 Lightweight garment (1-5)
4 On time (6)
9 Skilled worker (7)
10 Multiplied a number by itself (7)
11 Flat-bottomed vessels (5)
12 Ancient harps (5)
14 Stuck together (5)
15 Allotted quantity (5)
17 Single-edged hunting knife (5)
18 Formation of troops (7)
20 Small ornament (7)
21 Gives in (6)
22 Slender; thin (6)

Down

1 Follows the position of (6)
2 Until now (8)
3 Exposes to danger (5)
5 Reconstruct (7)
6 Bleak upland (4)
7 Buys and sells goods (6)
8 Tools; utensils (11)
13 Rouse again (8)
14 Wreath of flowers (7)
15 Nauseous (6)
16 Room attached to a church (6)
17 Verge (5)
19 Sharpen; improve (4)

Across

1 Scream (4)
3 Ocean (8)
9 Sailor (7)
10 Climbing or trailing plants (5)
11 Amusing (12)
13 Continent (6)
15 Locked lips with someone (6)
17 Not able to be confirmed (12)
20 Work at a loom (5)
21 A bird's feathers collectively (7)
22 Chaos (8)
23 Barrels (4)

Down

1 Battered (8)
2 Opposite of best (5)
4 Spun-out filament of cotton (6)
5 Coming from outside (12)
6 People who rent property (7)
7 Portfolio (4)
8 Someone who sets up their own business (12)
12 Laziness (8)
14 Antlers (anag.) (7)
16 Small depression in the flesh (6)
18 A pair of something (5)
19 Inspired by reverence (4)

CROSSWORD 82

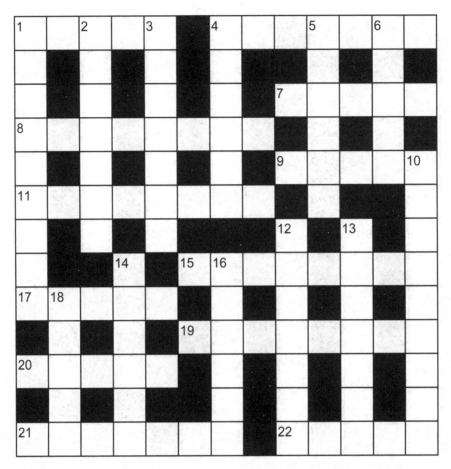

Across

1 Parts (anag.) (5)
4 A percussion instrument (7)
7 Rapidity of movement (5)
8 Enhancing; encouraging (8)
9 Apart from (5)
11 Text of an opera (8)
15 Increase (8)
17 Long for (5)
19 Last (8)
20 Expansive (5)
21 Amaze (7)
22 Herb (5)

Down

1 Constancy; steadiness (9)
2 Enclosed fortification (7)
3 Large flat dish (7)
4 Item that attracts iron (6)
5 Enforce compliance with (6)
6 Staple food (5)
10 Skill (9)
12 Mobile phone (7)
13 Stonework (7)
14 Wild horse (6)
16 Grabbed (6)
18 Peers (5)

CROSSWORD 83

Across

1 Silly person (4)
3 Spatters with liquid (8)
9 One of the archangels (7)
10 Last (5)
11 Haul (3)
12 The papal court (5)
13 Make a physical or mental effort (5)
15 Imitative of the past (5)
17 Welcome (5)
18 Golf peg (3)
19 Large crow (5)
20 Make obsolete (7)
21 Deceiving (8)
22 Mountain system in Europe (4)

Down

1 Given to thievery (5-8)
2 U-shaped curve in a river (5)
4 Royal house (6)
5 Loving (12)
6 Number of years in a century (7)
7 Conscious knowledge of oneself (4-9)
8 Dispirited (12)
14 Herb related to parsley (7)
16 Confused or disconcerted (6)
18 Lag behind (5)

CROSSWORD 84

Across

1 Skin irritation (4)
3 Sharply defined (5-3)
9 Clear mess away (5,2)
10 Blood vessels (5)
11 Relation by marriage (7-2-3)
14 Pull at (3)
16 Cuban folk dance (5)
17 E.g. Hedwig in Harry Potter (3)
18 Quarrelsome and uncooperative (12)
21 Ball of lead (5)
22 Sleep (4-3)
23 Ability to meet liabilities (8)
24 Hearing organs (4)

Down

1 Sit on eggs (of a bird) (8)
2 Doctrine; system of beliefs (5)
4 Remove branches (3)
5 Beneficial (12)
6 The Windy City (7)
7 Critical examination (4)
8 Unkind; unsympathetic (12)
12 Manor (anag.) (5)
13 Close groups (8)
15 Not sudden (7)
19 Dramatic musical work (5)
20 Primates (4)
22 Unit of time (abbrev.) (3)

CROSSWORD 85

Across

1 Most pleased (8)

5 What you walk on (4)

9 Jump over (5)

10 In front (5)

11 Fellow national (10)

14 Expressing regret (6)

15 Cutting or thrusting weapons (6)

17 Provisional explanation (10)

20 Game of chance (5)

21 Hang with cloth (5)

22 Subsequently (4)

23 Lively dance for two people (8)

Down

1 Where bees are kept (4)

2 Edible fruit (4)

3 Explanatory section of a book (12)

4 Maxim (6)

6 For all time (8)

7 Orderliness (8)

8 Lacking tolerance or flexibility (6-6)

12 Forbid (8)

13 Retort (8)

16 Spanish title for a married woman (6)

18 First light (4)

19 Short note or reminder (4)

Across

7 Opposite of after (6)
8 Immature insects (6)
9 Pal (4)
10 Brief summary (8)
11 Servile (7)
13 Sudden attack (5)
15 Cry out loudly (5)
16 Hot-tasting food dishes (7)
18 Recollected (8)
19 Bursts (4)
21 Young hog (6)
22 Occurring every seven days (6)

Down

1 Wire lattice (4)
2 Measurable by a common standard (13)
3 Mocking (7)
4 Make less sharp (5)
5 Code-breaker (13)
6 Steer (8)
12 Physically strong and active (8)
14 Insult (3-4)
17 Lists (anag.) (5)
20 Light in shade (4)

CROSSWORD 87

Across

1 Saturated (6)
7 Plant with decorative leaves (8)
8 Seed vessel (3)
9 Art of growing dwarfed trees (6)
10 Monetary unit of South Africa (4)
11 Roman cloaks (5)
13 Soldiers who fought on horseback (7)
15 Expeditions to observe animals (7)
17 Glazed earthenware (5)
21 Block a decision (4)
22 Robberies (6)
23 Mischievous sprite (3)
24 Lack of hair (8)
25 Bronzed (6)

Down

1 Marked effect (6)
2 Bloodsucking insect (6)
3 Common garden flower (5)
4 Far-reaching; thorough (7)
5 Study the night sky (8)
6 Jogger (6)
12 Large snake (8)
14 Walks very stealthily (7)
16 Stadiums (6)
18 Insole (anag.) (6)
19 Three-legged support for a camera (6)
20 Robbery (5)

Across

1 Highest point (11)
9 Long flat piece of timber (5)
10 Large (3)
11 Go over again (5)
12 Relating to birth (5)
13 Love song (8)
16 An opening (8)
18 Lumberjack (5)
21 Striped animal (5)
22 Male sheep (3)
23 Bolivian city (2,3)
24 Component parts (11)

Down

2 Imaginary creature (7)
3 Soaking up (7)
4 Approached (6)
5 Spoken for (5)
6 Circle a planet (5)
7 Keyboard instrument (11)
8 Form into a cluster (11)
14 Make mentally fatigued (7)
15 Small fast ship (7)
17 Burst a balloon (6)
19 Lady (5)
20 Measuring stick (5)

CROSSWORD 89

Across

7 Be overcome with laughter (8)
8 Encourage in wrongdoing (4)
9 Capital of Peru (4)
10 Have a wavy motion (8)
11 Suggested a course of action (7)
12 Concave roofs (5)
15 Municipalities (5)
17 Ebbs (7)
20 Name for New York City (3,5)
22 Sound of a snake (4)
23 Mischievous sprite (4)
24 Terraced (anag.) (8)

Down

1 Emulated (6)
2 The flying of aircraft (8)
3 Egg white (7)
4 Unwanted plants (5)
5 Dividing boundary (4)
6 Fortitude (6)
13 Make too excited (8)
14 Refutes; sends back (7)
16 Detestable (6)
18 Christian festival (6)
19 Flash of light (5)
21 Diving seabirds (4)

Across

1 Extend beyond a surface (8)

5 Curse; solemn promise (4)

8 Cease being awake (5)

9 Perfectly (7)

10 Largest anthropoid ape (7)

12 Science of matter and energy (7)

14 Vanquish (7)

16 River in Africa (7)

18 Finery (7)

19 Make fun of someone (5)

20 Chopped (4)

21 People who shape horseshoes (8)

Down

1 Time gone by (4)

2 Unidirectional (3-3)

3 Reject (9)

4 Activities (6)

6 Form of a gene (6)

7 Forceful blow (8)

11 Fresh precipitation (9)

12 Type of restaurant (8)

13 Regime (anag.) (6)

14 Large insect (6)

15 Refined in manner (6)

17 State of confusion (4)

CROSSWORD 91

Across

1 Where bees are kept (6)
5 Bland soft food (3)
7 Cost (5)
8 Enchanting (7)
9 Ten more than forty (5)
10 Limping (8)
12 Anxious (6)
14 Bed coverings (6)
17 Verifying (8)
18 Suitably (5)
20 Wealthy (4-3)
21 Layer (anag.) (5)
22 Longing (3)
23 Multiply by three (6)

Down

2 Military unit (7)
3 Careless; rash (8)
4 Petty quarrel (4)
5 Type of pheasant (7)
6 Ancient parchment (7)
7 Flat surface (5)
11 Brawny (8)
12 Normally (7)
13 Oriental (7)
15 Melodious (7)
16 Requiring much mastication (5)
19 Utter a loud scream (4)

Across

1 Expressing disapproval of (11)
9 Amide (anag.) (5)
10 Compete (3)
11 Plantain lily (5)
12 Divide; separate (5)
13 Borough of New York City (8)
16 Handheld firework (8)
18 Passage between rows of seats (5)
21 Hank of wool (5)
22 Twitch (3)
23 Unwarranted (5)
24 Pretentious display (11)

Down

2 Hearing range (7)
3 Comments (7)
4 Arrange laws systematically (6)
5 Melts (5)
6 Maritime (5)
7 Residents (11)
8 Eating establishments (11)
14 Divide into three parts (7)
15 Quick musical tempo (7)
17 Expert in a particular subject (6)
19 Religious groups (5)
20 Draw or bring out (5)

CROSSWORD 93

Across

1 Stinging weed (6)
4 Smear or blur (6)
9 Green vegetation (7)
10 Central cell part (7)
11 People not ordained (5)
12 Tests (5)
14 Well-known (5)
15 Stage play (5)
17 Bout of extravagant shopping (5)
18 Joined to something (7)
20 Finished (3,4)
21 Holds up (6)
22 Rode a bike (6)

Down

1 Books (6)
2 Mexican pancake (8)
3 Very bad (5)
5 Walked quickly (7)
6 Delude (4)
7 Deletes (6)
8 Nostalgic (11)
13 Consent (8)
14 Weakly; dimly (7)
15 Covered in cloth (6)
16 Looked searchingly (6)
17 Saline (5)
19 Cheek (4)

Across

1 Black waterbird (4)

3 Animals with long necks (8)

9 Ideas (7)

10 Surpass (5)

11 Consumed (of food) (5)

12 Least fresh (7)

13 Checked; examined (6)

15 Quantum of electromagnetic energy (6)

17 State of disorder (7)

18 Lover of Juliet (5)

20 Balearic island (5)

21 Irreligious (7)

22 Narrowly avoided accident (4,4)

23 Depend upon (4)

Down

1 Close mental application (13)

2 Group of eight (5)

4 Take a firm stand (6)

5 Therapeutic use of plant extracts (12)

6 Item of furniture (7)

7 Impulsively (13)

8 Comical tuner (anag.) (12)

14 Endurance (7)

16 The words of a song (6)

19 Type of large deer (5)

Across

7 Relating to construction (8)
8 Belonging to us (4)
9 Endure; animal (4)
10 Unfurled (8)
11 Hopes to achieve (7)
12 Sulks (5)
15 Narcotics (5)
17 Brutality (7)
20 Choosing to take up or follow (8)
22 Make a choice through a ballot (4)
23 Look slyly (4)
24 Tied up (8)

Down

1 Insurgents (6)
2 Violently attacking (a building) (8)
3 Guarantees (7)
4 Frightening (5)
5 Immaterial part of a person (4)
6 Current of air (6)
13 Summary (8)
14 Warship (7)
16 Steering mechanism of a boat (6)
18 Unsteady gait (6)
19 Eating plans (5)
21 Minute surface opening (4)

Across

1 Unrestrained (11)
9 Large African antelope (5)
10 Cry (3)
11 Performed on stage (5)
12 Compound tissue in vascular plants (5)
13 Condemn publicly (8)
16 Food of the gods (8)
18 Leg bone (5)
21 Port-au-Prince is the capital here (5)
22 Long period of time (3)
23 Friend (Spanish) (5)
24 Ongoing disagreement (11)

Down

2 Tidies (7)
3 Necessary (7)
4 Sloping (of a typeface) (6)
5 Alphabetical list in a book (5)
6 Supporting frame used by an artist (5)
7 Female relation (11)
8 Feeling of hatred (11)
14 One of two gaps in a shirt (7)
15 Helps (7)
17 Sheep known for its wool (6)
19 Shout of appreciation (5)
20 Change (5)

Across

1 Snares; bags (4)

3 Renounce (8)

9 Tell a story (7)

10 Dairy product (5)

11 Flour dough used in cooking (5)

12 Treason (anag.) (7)

13 Next after seventh (6)

15 Deprive of food (6)

17 Explanations (7)

18 Flaring stars (5)

20 Horse sound (5)

21 Pays no attention to (7)

22 Choosing from various sources (8)

23 Repudiate (4)

Down

1 Absence (13)

2 Rotates (5)

4 Ukrainian port (6)

5 Without parallel (6,2,4)

6 Voter (7)

7 Pitilessly (13)

8 Extremely harmful (12)

14 Icy (7)

16 Birthplace of St Francis (6)

19 Edge or border (5)

Across

1 Loud rushing noise (6)
5 Steal (3)
7 Tremble (5)
8 Part exchange for something new (5-2)
9 Large motor vehicle (5)
10 State of the USA (8)
12 Routed (anag.) (6)
14 Throngs (6)
17 Having a striking beauty (8)
18 Small plant-sucking insect (5)
20 E.g. Tuesday (7)
21 Walks awkwardly (5)
22 Method; road (3)
23 Punctuation mark (6)

Down

2 Courageous woman (7)
3 Not genuine (8)
4 Cease moving (4)
5 Repudiated (7)
6 Summons with the hand (7)
7 Go stealthily or furtively (5)
11 Seriousness (8)
12 Deny any responsibility for (7)
13 Firmly; closely (7)
15 Instruct (7)
16 Moves like a liquid (5)
19 Concave roof (4)

Across

1 Second-hand (8)
5 Male sheep (pl.) (4)
9 School of fish (5)
10 Danger (5)
11 Removed water from (10)
14 Rejuvenates (6)
15 Duty or tax (6)
17 Society led by men (10)
20 Type of bus (5)
21 Amplify a signal (5)
22 Puts down (4)
23 Mind reader (8)

Down

1 Annoying person (4)
2 Greek god of love (4)
3 Boxing class division (12)
4 Relishes (6)
6 Small landing and take-off area (8)
7 Become firm (8)
8 Easy to converse with (12)
12 Hot and humid (8)
13 Unstable (8)
16 Work hard; menial worker (6)
18 Garment of ancient Rome (4)
19 Engrave with acid (4)

CROSSWORD 100

Across

1 Dejection (11)
9 Remove errors from software (5)
10 Religious sister (3)
11 Stiff (5)
12 Five lines on which music is written (5)
13 Lumberjack's tool (8)
16 Highly seasoned smoked beef (8)
18 Very skilled at something (5)
21 Bring into a line (5)
22 Cause friction (3)
23 Group of bees (5)
24 Daring; bold (11)

Down

2 Witty saying (7)
3 Stuffing (7)
4 Cloud of gas in space (6)
5 Borders (5)
6 Latin American dance (5)
7 Word used by magicians (11)
8 Deliberate (11)
14 Type of ship (7)
15 Reindeer (7)
17 Struck by overwhelming shock (6)
19 Implant (5)
20 Sense experience (5)

Across

1 Repeat an action (4)
3 Type of tooth (8)
9 Clique (7)
10 Loose overall (5)
11 Clearly evident (12)
14 And not (3)
16 Ice home (5)
17 Damage (3)
18 Reparation (12)
21 Live by (5)
22 Combined metals (7)
23 Increases (8)
24 Trees of the genus Ulmus (4)

Down

1 Disappearing gradually (8)
2 Piece of information (5)
4 Anger (3)
5 Untimely (12)
6 Dilemma (7)
7 Sovereign prince (4)
8 Principal face of a building (12)
12 Bird claw (5)
13 Explosive shells (8)
15 Rampaging (7)
19 Extremely happy period (5)
20 Spanish sparkling wine (4)
22 Statute (3)

Across

1 Tasteless (5)
4 Unfortunate (7)
7 Players who form a team (5)
8 Precludes (8)
9 Medieval contest (5)
11 Whole numbers (8)
15 Fugitives (8)
17 Urges on (5)
19 Having a sweet nature (8)
20 Businesses (5)
21 Sports ground (7)
22 Bed cover (5)

Down

1 Offensively self-assertive (9)
2 Official pardon (7)
3 Move apart (7)
4 Warming device (6)
5 Alcoholic drink (6)
6 Long-necked birds (5)
10 Very sensitive (of information) (3,6)
12 Joins in matrimony (7)
13 Green vegetation (7)
14 Prepared (6)
16 Division of a group (6)
18 Inapt (anag.) (5)

Across

7 Sullen and gloomy (6)
8 Lots of (6)
9 Unwanted wild plant (4)
10 Husband of one's daughter (3-2-3)
11 Factory for casting metal (7)
13 These protect you from rain (5)
15 Stitched (5)
16 Hit with the fist (7)
18 Short heavy club (8)
19 Labyrinth (4)
21 Way of doing something (6)
22 Digging for minerals (6)

Down

1 Bird of peace (4)
2 50th anniversary of marriage (6,7)
3 Tough questions (7)
4 Backbone (5)
5 Action of strengthening (13)
6 Sit with legs wide apart (8)
12 Burden with too much work (8)
14 E.g. Jones or Smith (7)
17 Burns the surface of (5)
20 Zest; liveliness (4)

Across

1 Curved shapes (4)
3 Shrewdly (8)
9 E.g. a bishop (7)
10 Foresee or predict (5)
11 Foreboding (12)
13 Exclusive stories (6)
15 Brandy distilled from cherries (6)
17 Binoculars (5,7)
20 Pale orange tropical fruit (5)
21 Forbidden by law (7)
22 Cutting instrument (8)
23 Push; poke (4)

Down

1 Hand clapping (8)
2 Inexpensive (5)
4 Oozed (6)
5 Impregnable (12)
6 Fully occupy (7)
7 Three feet (4)
8 Butterfly larvae (12)
12 Made a high-pitched sound (8)
14 Japanese art of paper folding (7)
16 Less attractive (6)
18 Sweet substance (5)
19 Matures (4)

Across

1 Cook in the oven (4)
3 Medieval weapon (8)
9 Small dissenting group (7)
10 Spacious (5)
11 Unpleasant (12)
14 Ignited (3)
16 Humiliate (5)
17 Jewel (3)
18 Caused by disease (12)
21 Funny person (5)
22 Electric appliance (7)
23 Unsubstantiated (8)
24 Walked or stepped (4)

Down

1 Confuse (8)
2 Strikes with the foot (5)
4 Flee (3)
5 Stretched out completely (12)
6 Distribute illicitly (7)
7 Routes; methods (4)
8 Pertaining to a person's life (12)
12 Electronic message (5)
13 Beseeched (8)
15 Emotional shocks (7)
19 Programmer (5)
20 Protective crust over a wound (4)
22 Form of public transport (3)

Across

7 Buccaneer (6)

8 Removed unwanted plants (6)

9 Opposite of right (4)

10 Principal (8)

11 Leaving gaps; padding (7)

13 Shapes (5)

15 Experiences through touch (5)

16 An acted riddle (7)

18 Use of threats to persuade a person to do something (8)

19 Select; choose (4)

21 Remained expectantly (6)

22 Abandon a plan (6)

Down

1 Evergreen coniferous tree (4)

2 Quality of being individual (13)

3 Decline (7)

4 Pointed weapon (5)

5 Compiler of a dictionary (13)

6 Made still (8)

12 Tooth (8)

14 E.g. from Beijing (7)

17 Discovers (5)

20 Underground chamber (4)

Across

1 Home (5)
4 Dispute or competition (7)
7 Small seat (5)
8 Source of annoyance (8)
9 Throw forcefully (5)
11 Unclean (8)
15 Sewage discharged into water (8)
17 Train tracks (5)
19 Process of sticking to a surface (8)
20 Amusing people (5)
21 Greek white wine (7)
22 Wrinkles in the skin (5)

Down

1 Relating to the ear (9)
2 Intimidate (7)
3 Feeling of great happiness (7)
4 Possibility (6)
5 Gossip or idle talk (6)
6 Item of cutlery (5)
10 Sticky (9)
12 Exuberantly joyful (7)
13 Meat from a deer (7)
14 Swords (6)
16 Soft felt hat (6)
18 Hard chalcedony (5)

CROSSWORD 108

Across

1 Way of speaking (8)
5 This grows on your head (4)
8 Parts of legs (5)
9 Boats (7)
10 Released from a duty (7)
12 Throb (7)
14 Pertaining to the skull (7)
16 Volcanic crater (7)
18 Express strong condemnation of (7)
19 Circular in shape (5)
20 Extinct bird (4)
21 Search for minerals (8)

Down

1 Elapse (of time) (4)
2 Nasal (6)
3 Self-confidence (9)
4 Hot drink containing caffeine (6)
6 Among (6)
7 Remaining (8)
11 Living things (9)
12 Went before (8)
13 Inclined (6)
14 Occupation or profession (6)
15 Attribute to (6)
17 Change (4)

CROSSWORD 109

Across

1 Small pet rodent (6)
5 Action of making use of something (6)
8 Having no money (4)
9 Card game (8)
10 God of love (5)
11 Cut of beef (7)
14 Regrettably (13)
16 Type of polish (7)
18 Suspends (5)
20 Spread out untidily (8)
22 Trigonometric function (4)
23 Physical item (6)
24 Quantity (6)

Down

2 Fluent use of language (9)
3 Tortilla rolled around a filling (7)
4 Good fortune (4)
5 Creatures with one horn (8)
6 Pipes (5)
7 Beer container (3)
12 Careful work or effort (9)
13 Not curly (of hair) (8)
15 Wooden bar across a window (7)
17 Catch; lure (5)
19 Restrain (4)
21 Bat (anag.) (3)

Across

1 Play boisterously (6)
7 Tongue (8)
8 Decay (3)
9 Dual audio (6)
10 Gardening tools used for weeding (4)
11 Trench (5)
13 Person devoted to love (7)
15 Distant runner-up in a horse race (4-3)
17 Light canoe (5)
21 Days before major events (4)
22 Plan; strategy (6)
23 Argument against something (3)
24 Mythical creature (8)
25 Unfriendly in manner (6)

Down

1 Disallow; prevent (6)
2 Beginning (6)
3 Office records keeper (5)
4 Imparts knowledge (7)
5 Elation (8)
6 Wading birds (6)
12 Covered walk in a convent (8)
14 Stronghold (7)
16 Taxes (6)
18 Woody-stemmed plants (6)
19 Organ (6)
20 Mark or wear thin (5)

CROSSWORD 111

Across

1 Opposite of pull (4)
3 Removing from the premises (8)
9 Sophisticated hair style (7)
10 Long rods (5)
11 Science of space travel (12)
13 Reason for not doing something (6)
15 Substance present in cereal grains (6)
17 Spanish adventurer (12)
20 Dwelling (5)
21 Set apart (7)
22 More attractive (8)
23 Lots (anag.) (4)

Down

1 Boxes (8)
2 Holy person (5)
4 One who wantonly destroys property (6)
5 Surrender (12)
6 Unlawful (7)
7 Current of air (4)
8 Irrelevant (12)
12 Most annoyed (8)
14 Sense of resolution (7)
16 Godlike (6)
18 Speak in a slow manner (5)
19 Hew (4)

Across

1 Having a lot to do (4)
3 Complying with orders (8)
9 Belief (7)
10 Polite address for a woman (5)
11 Young newt (3)
12 Loop with a running knot (5)
13 Ellipses (5)
15 Underground enlarged stem (5)
17 Small venomous snake (5)
18 Imitate (3)
19 Impair (5)
20 Perform in an exaggerated manner (7)
21 Broke down food (8)
22 Room in a jail (4)

Down

1 Overwhelmed with sorrow (6-7)
2 Move (5)
4 Yellow fruit (6)
5 Showed (12)
6 Last in a series (7)
7 Unpredictable (13)
8 Type of cloud (12)
14 Prodding with the elbow (7)
16 Belonging to an earlier time (6)
18 With speed (5)

CROSSWORD 113

Across

1 Structured set of information (8)
5 Close by (4)
9 Three-note chord (5)
10 Change (5)
11 Exuberance (10)
14 Introduction (4-2)
15 Served (anag.) (6)
17 Series of links on a web page (10)
20 Cloth woven from flax (5)
21 Bump (5)
22 Small stream (4)
23 Woodwind instrument (8)

Down

1 Dark brown oval fruit (4)
2 Work hard (4)
3 Process of enlarging one's muscles (12)
4 Bitterly (6)
6 Fairness (8)
7 People with auburn hair (8)
8 Skilled joiner (12)
12 Spherical (8)
13 Fatherly (8)
16 Go from one place to another (6)
18 Cut (of grass) (4)
19 Comedy sketch (4)

CROSSWORD 114

Across

1 Feeling of expectation (4)
3 Access code (8)
9 Discourse (7)
10 Computer memory units (5)
11 Act of influencing someone deviously (12)
13 Metamorphic rock (6)
15 Arch of the foot (6)
17 Antique; not modern (3-9)
20 Attendant upon God (5)
21 Word opposite in meaning to another (7)
22 Social insect (8)
23 Stylish (4)

Down

1 Flag position to indicate mourning (4-4)
2 Brown nut (5)
4 Ancient or well established (3-3)
5 Strengthen; confirm (12)
6 Distant settlement (7)
7 Shallow food container (4)
8 Resolutely (12)
12 Large outbreak of a disease (8)
14 E.g. fluorine or chlorine (7)
16 Get away from (6)
18 A number between an eighth and a tenth (5)
19 Whip (4)

CROSSWORD 115

Across

1 Having pains (4)
3 Allocated (8)
9 Pasta pockets (7)
10 Punctuation mark (5)
11 Person who receives office visitors (12)
14 Large body of water (3)
16 Delete (5)
17 Drink a little (3)
18 Best starting placement in a motor race (4,8)
21 Verse (5)
22 Link together (7)
23 Supervisor (8)
24 Agitate (4)

Down

1 Device for spraying paint (8)
2 Total disorder (5)
4 Snow runner (3)
5 Awkward (12)
6 Goddess of retribution (7)
7 Dull (4)
8 Entirety (12)
12 Adult insect stage (5)
13 Unmarried woman (8)
15 Capable of relieving pain (7)
19 Maladroit (5)
20 Therefore (Latin) (4)
22 Signal for action (3)

Across

7 Centre (8)

8 Trees that bear acorns (4)

9 Very tired (4)

10 Streams of rain (8)

11 Renews membership (7)

12 Quick and active (5)

15 Sowed (anag.) (5)

17 Bring to life (7)

20 Most dirty (8)

22 Give a particular title to (4)

23 Small mountain lake (4)

24 Conversation between two people (3-2-3)

Down

1 Type of basic aerial (6)

2 Financial supporters (8)

3 Sorting through; separating (7)

4 Keep (5)

5 Position adopted for a photo (4)

6 Ice shoes (6)

13 Mammal that chews the cud (8)

14 Needleworker (7)

16 Of the eye (6)

18 Domesticating (6)

19 Lure an animal into a trap (5)

21 Sand hill (4)

CROSSWORD 117

Across

1 Front of a building; false display (6)
5 Young dog (3)
7 Grind teeth together (5)
8 Insect body segment (7)
9 Clean with a brush (5)
10 Physical power (8)
12 Depression from a meteor impact (6)
14 Horn (6)
17 Overcame (8)
18 Assertion (5)
20 Small toothed whale (7)
21 Jumps in the air (5)
22 Layer of a folded material (3)
23 Injure (6)

Down

2 One who settles a dispute (7)
3 Insisted upon (8)
4 Low platform for a lectern (4)
5 Mythical bird (7)
6 Devise beforehand (7)
7 Midges (5)
11 Fleet of ships (8)
12 Routine dental examination (5-2)
13 Affably (7)
15 Employment vacancy (7)
16 Touches down (5)
19 Dame (anag.) (4)

Across

1 Disengage (6)
4 Frightens (6)
9 Music player (7)
10 Preserved in brine or vinegar (7)
11 Large black birds (5)
12 Card game (5)
14 Wept (5)
15 Time when life begins (5)
17 Group (5)
18 Drug that relieves pain (7)
20 Walk aimlessly (7)
21 Put right (6)
22 Return to a former condition (6)

Down

1 Dispirit (6)
2 Assume control of (4,4)
3 Solids with six equal square faces (5)
5 Agreement (7)
6 Complain bitterly (4)
7 Assorted; various (6)
8 Tries out novel ideas (11)
13 Having many parts (8)
14 Intense (7)
15 Drinking container (6)
16 Imminent danger (6)
17 Hold responsible (5)
19 Inner surface of the hand (4)

Across

1 Decomposes (6)
5 Change (6)
8 Condemn to destruction (4)
9 Branch of metaphysics (8)
10 Furnaces (5)
11 Laughing like a donkey (7)
14 Misplaced in time or date (13)
16 Tardiest (7)
18 Immature insects (5)
20 Pink wading bird (8)
22 Visage (4)
23 Exhausts (6)
24 Belief in a god or gods (6)

Down

2 Affecting the feelings (9)
3 Yearbook (7)
4 Before long (4)
5 Moving as fast as possible (8)
6 Interruption (5)
7 Atmospheric murk; obscure (3)
12 Bothersome people (9)
13 Gifts (8)
15 Mix a deck of cards (7)
17 Ladies (5)
19 Publish in an online forum (4)
21 One circuit of a track (3)

Across

1 Drink (6)
5 Nine plus one (3)
7 Joyous and happy (5)
8 Nestle up against (7)
9 Increase in size (5)
10 Impetus (8)
12 Takes along (6)
14 Morally admirable (6)
17 Audacity (8)
18 Erased (5)
20 Period of prolonged dryness (7)
21 Decapod crustaceans (5)
22 Louse egg (3)
23 Refund (6)

Down

2 Imaginary scary creature (7)
3 Be envious of (8)
4 Close-fitting undergarments (4)
5 Prepare for printing (7)
6 Make ineffective (7)
7 Lists of restaurants dishes (5)
11 Portend (8)
12 Among (7)
13 Examine (7)
15 Axe (7)
16 Listens to (5)
19 Haul (4)

CROSSWORD 121

Across

1 Secondary personality (5,3)
5 Time periods (4)
8 Bring together (5)
9 Molar tooth (7)
10 Coat; decorate lavishly (7)
12 Throw away (7)
14 Letters (anag.) (7)
16 Bed covering (7)
18 Take out (7)
19 Published false statement (5)
20 Compassionate (4)
21 Publicly recommend (8)

Down

1 Fever (4)
2 Groups of three (6)
3 Capital of Iceland (9)
4 Silenced (6)
6 Bone in the forearm (6)
7 Wine and soda water mix (8)
11 Lowest female singing voice (9)
12 Dawn (8)
13 Licentious; deliberate (6)
14 Specified (6)
15 11th Greek letter (6)
17 Merriment (4)

Across

1 Dull pain (4)
3 Hopefulness about the future (8)
9 Continue (5,2)
10 Gives as a reference (5)
11 University teacher (3)
12 Obsession (5)
13 Muscular contraction (5)
15 External (5)
17 Crustacean like a shrimp (5)
18 Herb; regret (3)
19 Command (5)
20 Surpass (7)
21 Lift (8)
22 Temporary outside shelter (4)

Down

1 Liable to get injured (8-5)
2 Wading bird (5)
4 Country in Central America (6)
5 Immeasurably (12)
6 Recites as a chant (7)
7 Ineptitude in running a business (13)
8 Valetudinarianism (12)
14 Person of high rank (7)
16 Dinner jacket (6)
18 Indian monetary unit (5)

CROSSWORD 123

Across

1 Elevated off the ground (6)
4 Sailing barge (6)
9 Colonnade (7)
10 Steep in (7)
11 Killer whales (5)
12 Telephones (5)
14 Young bird (5)
15 Perhaps (5)
17 Grasslike marsh plant (5)
18 Imaginary mischievous sprite (7)
20 Ascended (7)
21 Hate (6)
22 Assert (6)

Down

1 Subatomic particle such as an electron (6)
2 Savage fierceness (8)
3 Lives (anag.) (5)
5 Knoll (7)
6 Lion noise (4)
7 Songlike cries (6)
8 Chance concurrence of events (11)
13 Praiseworthy (8)
14 Basements (7)
15 Accosted; robbed (6)
16 Hawk (6)
17 Rinse out with water (5)
19 Door by which you leave a building (4)

Across

1 Widespread (4)
3 Fruit sugar (8)
9 Schedule of activities (7)
10 Encounters (5)
11 Overwhelmingly compelling (12)
14 By way of (3)
16 Country in southern Asia (5)
17 Legume (3)
18 Very determined (6-6)
21 Wild dog of Australia (5)
22 Not limited to one class (7)
23 Fervently (8)
24 Biblical garden (4)

Down

1 Respite (8)
2 Fine powdery foodstuff (5)
4 Strong spirit (3)
5 Blends; mixtures (12)
6 Coincide partially (7)
7 Otherwise (4)
8 Scolding (8-4)
12 Move sideways (5)
13 Stringed musical instrument (8)
15 Arranged neatly (7)
19 Challenged (5)
20 Creative thought (4)
22 Cohere (3)

CROSSWORD 125

Across

1 Source of caviar (6)
7 Not extreme (8)
8 Become firm (3)
9 Group of mountains (6)
10 Dove sounds (4)
11 Petulant (5)
13 Cleaning item (7)
15 Belgian language (7)
17 Eats like a bird (5)
21 Pose (anag.) (4)
22 Fly an aircraft (6)
23 Ground condensation (3)
24 Long-tailed parrot (8)
25 Scolded strongly (6)

Down

1 Container (6)
2 Dye used as a test of acidity (6)
3 Wrong (5)
4 Building (7)
5 Pamphlet (8)
6 Caress (6)
12 Relating to time (8)
14 Gets out (7)
16 Margin of safety (6)
18 Recognition (6)
19 Displayed (6)
20 Enumerates (5)

Across

1 Groups of eight (6)
5 Empty space between two objects (3)
7 High renown (5)
8 Sporting dog (7)
9 Small circular bands (5)
10 Potentially self-destructive (8)
12 Upper classes (6)
14 Attractive (6)
17 Reasoning logically (8)
18 Flowers (5)
20 Citadel in Moscow (7)
21 Tall and thin (5)
22 Attempt to do (3)
23 Cord (6)

Down

2 Pack cue (anag.) (7)
3 Deception (8)
4 Decant (4)
5 Flexible athlete (7)
6 Herb (7)
7 Fit with glass (5)
11 Heated exchange of views (8)
12 Epicure (7)
13 Loudly (7)
15 Mental strain (7)
16 Annoying (5)
19 Exposes to natural light (4)

CROSSWORD 127

Across

1 Constructs (6)
4 Ice homes (6)
9 Display unit; supervise (7)
10 Relaxes (7)
11 Satisfied a desire (5)
12 Made a mistake (5)
14 Angered; irritated (5)
15 Spiritual nourishment (5)
17 Portion of a play (5)
18 Skill (7)
20 Abandons a plan (7)
21 Flood (6)
22 Exchanged goods or services (6)

Down

1 Bewilder (6)
2 Action of setting something on fire (8)
3 Old-fashioned (5)
5 Grumbled (7)
6 Portent (4)
7 Perceived (6)
8 Tendency to disintegrate (11)
13 Booked in advance (8)
14 Incrementing; elevating (7)
15 Slightly annoyed (6)
16 Stopped (6)
17 Absolute (5)
19 Invalid; void (4)

Across

1 Alludes to (6)
7 Mythical sea creatures (8)
8 Place where one sees animals (3)
9 Had a strong and unpleasant smell (6)
10 Suffers (4)
11 Stomach exercise (3-2)
13 Opposite (7)
15 Fishing boat (7)
17 Moves back and forth (5)
21 Fly high (4)
22 Calculating instrument (6)
23 Adult males (3)
24 Remove a monarch (8)
25 Type of engine (6)

Down

1 Barber's tools (6)
2 Small flower (6)
3 Hazy (5)
4 Buying and selling (7)
5 Hot pepper (8)
6 Mixes up or confuses (6)
12 Undeserving (8)
14 E.g. shrimp or crab (7)
16 Firmly established (6)
18 Universe (6)
19 Gesture (6)
20 Trudged through water (5)

CROSSWORD 129

Across

7 Quick reply (8)
8 Lubricates (4)
9 Spice made from nutmeg (4)
10 Disciple (8)
11 Moved round an axis (7)
12 Solicits custom (5)
15 Malice (5)
17 Aerial rescue (7)
20 Push button outside a house (8)
22 Surplus (4)
23 Chinese dynasty (4)
24 Womanly (8)

Down

1 Red salad fruit (6)
2 Pertinent (8)
3 Confounded (7)
4 Move sneakily (5)
5 Crazy (informal) (4)
6 Although (6)
13 Accommodating (8)
14 Certificate (7)
16 Irrational fear (6)
18 Articulate; eloquent (6)
19 Muscular (5)
21 Pieces of cloth (4)

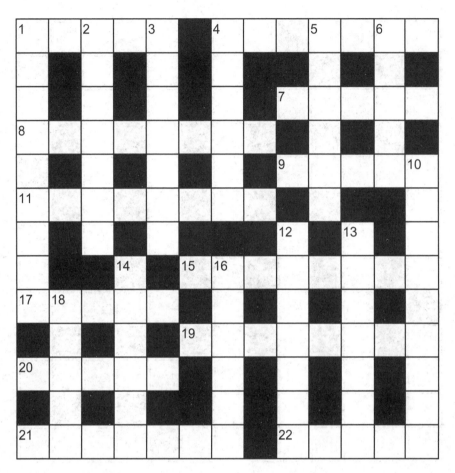

Across

1 Military walk (5)

4 Mass of flowers (7)

7 Fad (5)

8 People of no note (8)

9 Large-headed pieces of metal (5)

11 Withdraws (8)

15 Reprove (8)

17 Authoritative proclamation (5)

19 Type of pasta often eaten with cheese (8)

20 Period of keeping awake to pray (5)

21 Very low temperature fridge (7)

22 Captivates (5)

Down

1 Large high-speed computer (9)

2 Burrowing rodents (7)

3 Progress (7)

4 Deprived of; lacking (6)

5 Squirt a liquid in short bursts (6)

6 Seeped (5)

10 Acts of observation (9)

12 Sovereign (7)

13 Hot wind blowing from North Africa (7)

14 Opposite of passive (6)

16 Buyer and seller (6)

18 Less moist (5)

CROSSWORD 131

Across

1 Brood (4)
3 Teacher (8)
9 Shock physically (5-2)
10 Attractively stylish (5)
11 Reticent; secretive (12)
13 Excuses of any kind (6)
15 Capital of Canada (6)
17 Food shop (12)
20 Undo a knot (5)
21 Exclusion from the workplace (7)
22 A period of 366 days (4,4)
23 Flightless birds (4)

Down

1 Composer or singer (8)
2 Musical instrument (5)
4 Bring into action (6)
5 Body of voters in a specified region (12)
6 Silk-like fabric (7)
7 Light beams from the sun (4)
8 Monotonously (12)
12 Tycoons (8)
14 Resistance to change (7)
16 Spanish rice dish (6)
18 Violent weather (5)
19 Contest between two people (4)

Across

1 Disease caused by a lack of thiamine (8)
5 Entry document (4)
8 Ray (5)
9 Pertaining to plants (7)
10 Large crustacean (7)
12 Musical ending (7)
14 Took the place of (7)
16 Marked by prosperity (of a past time) (7)
18 Late (7)
19 Later (5)
20 Turn or slide violently (of a vehicle) (4)
21 Additional book matter (8)

Down

1 Collide with (4)
2 Circled (6)
3 Obviously (9)
4 Mob (6)
6 Inborn (6)
7 Agreed (8)
11 Divide into two branches (9)
12 Buffers (8)
13 Garment part that covers an arm (6)
14 Straighten out (6)
15 Placed a plant in a container (6)
17 Proper (4)

CROSSWORD 133

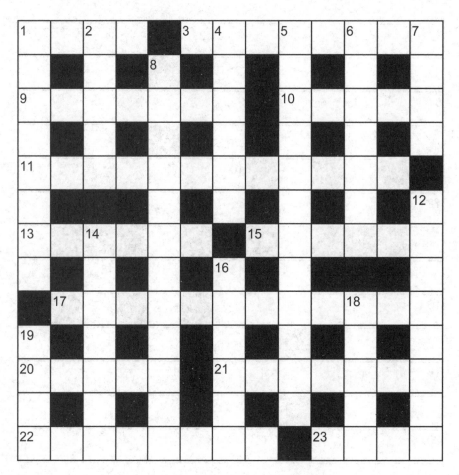

Across

1 Benefit of a job (4)
3 Yielded (8)
9 Decreased (7)
10 Swagger (5)
11 Use of words that mimic sounds (12)
13 E.g. time a tennis shot badly (6)
15 Infuriate (6)
17 Thriftily (12)
20 Be the same as (5)
21 Obviously (7)
22 Campaigner (8)
23 Long-running dispute (4)

Down

1 Acts in a play (8)
2 Wireless (5)
4 Extremely fashionable;
   scalding (3-3)
5 Unplugged (12)
6 Birthplace of Napoleon (7)
7 Facts and statistics
   collectively (4)
8 Now and then (12)
12 Naive or sentimental (4-4)
14 Yield (7)
16 Loose protective garments (6)
18 Big (5)
19 Swollen mark on flesh (4)

Across

1 Makes a bill law (6)
4 Fire-breathing monster (6)
9 Text accompanying a cartoon (7)
10 Relating to heat (7)
11 Any finger or toe (5)
12 Parts of the cerebrum (5)
14 Strong cords (5)
15 Lying flat (5)
17 Spree (5)
18 Plant with bright flowers (7)
20 Instructs (7)
21 Reverberated (6)
22 Piece of grassland (6)

Down

1 Encrypt (6)
2 Notes of a chord played in rapid succession (8)
3 Unexpected plot element (5)
5 Exposes (7)
6 Metric unit of mass (4)
7 Royal people (6)
8 Immoderate (11)
13 Split into subdivisions (8)
14 Get back together (7)
15 Small stone (6)
16 Change rapidly from one position to another (6)
17 Edge of a knife (5)
19 Long deep cut (4)

CROSSWORD 135

Across

1 Pieces of tough fibrous tissue (6)
7 Cloudy and dull (8)
8 Joke (3)
9 Wooden house (6)
10 Central (4)
11 Prevent access to something (5)
13 Trace (7)
15 Mends (7)
17 Large gathering of people (5)
21 Whirring sound (4)
22 Urge (6)
23 Hog (3)
24 An engraved design (8)
25 Move unsteadily (6)

Down

1 Majestic; wonderful (6)
2 Papal representative (6)
3 Makes dirty (5)
4 Insects with biting mouthparts (7)
5 Curved sword (8)
6 Putting a question to (6)
12 Presiding officer (8)
14 Momentarily (7)
16 Resembling a horse (6)
18 Yield (6)
19 Sharp knife (6)
20 Fire a weapon (5)

Across

1 Bean (6)
4 On the beach; on land (6)
9 Pin in a spinning wheel (7)
10 Loud and hoarse (7)
11 Regulations (5)
12 Biological taxonomic grouping (5)
14 Blunder (5)
15 Person who goes on long walks (5)
17 Damage the reputation of (5)
18 A rich mine; big prize (7)
20 Outburst of anger (7)
21 Next to (6)
22 More profound (6)

Down

1 Intense beams of light (6)
2 Severe traffic congestion (8)
3 Fashions; styles (5)
5 Flog; whip (7)
6 Toon (anag.) (4)
7 Survives; lives (6)
8 Document confirming an achievement (11)
13 Refer to famous people one knows (4-4)
14 Smiled broadly (7)
15 Mix socially (6)
16 Vibration (6)
17 From that time (5)
19 Common sense (4)

CROSSWORD 137

Across

1 Legendary tales (6)
7 Disloyal people (8)
8 Floor mat (3)
9 Victor (6)
10 Chemical salt used in dyeing (4)
11 Take part in combat (5)
13 Non-believer in God (7)
15 Reasons for thinking something (7)
17 Church songs (5)
21 Observe; notice (4)
22 Declares invalid (6)
23 Add together (3)
24 Joins up (8)
25 Pieces of furniture (6)

Down

1 A long way away (3,3)
2 Important person (6)
3 Rocky (5)
4 Attic rooms (7)
5 Plan of action (8)
6 Fakes (6)
12 Not quickly forgotten (8)
14 Progress (7)
16 Bird of prey (6)
18 Prayer book (6)
19 Mashes (anag.) (6)
20 Anxiety (5)

Across

1 Relating to stars (6)
5 Spread out awkwardly (6)
8 Sodium chloride (4)
9 Old toll road (8)
10 Eel-like fish (5)
11 Criminal (7)
14 Voice projection (13)
16 Restaurant serving roast meats (7)
18 Burn (5)
20 Yellowish edible seed (8)
22 Swerve (4)
23 Makes more attractive (6)
24 Tell off severely (6)

Down

2 Ongoing television serial (4,5)
3 Go back on (7)
4 Thin strip of wood (4)
5 One who lives through affliction (8)
6 Push away (5)
7 Frying pan (3)
12 Bankrupt (9)
13 Brings disorder to (8)
15 Reveal (7)
17 Clergyman (5)
19 Clothing (4)
21 Removed from sight (3)

CROSSWORD 139

Across

1 Natter (4)
3 Intellectual (8)
9 Capital of Kenya (7)
10 A written document (5)
11 Supply with; furnish (5)
12 Magnified view (5-2)
13 Outcast (6)
15 Lively Spanish dance (6)
17 Illness (7)
18 Make amends (5)
20 Inactive (5)
21 Agrees or corresponds (7)
22 All people (8)
23 Mark left from a wound (4)

Down

1 Very thoughtful (13)
2 Word of farewell (5)
4 Stupidity (6)
5 Thick-skinned herbivorous animal (12)
6 Abundantly supplied (7)
7 Computer program for writing documents (4,9)
8 In a self-satisfied manner (12)
14 Release someone from duty (7)
16 Scattered about untidily (6)
19 Topic (anag.) (5)

Across

1 Army unit (8)
5 Injure (4)
8 Second planet from the sun (5)
9 Become tense (7)
10 Signs up (7)
12 Jostled (7)
14 Divisions between groups of people (7)
16 Urgent (7)
18 Duty-bound (7)
19 Beneath (5)
20 Flightless bird (4)
21 Large celebration (8)

Down

1 Talk wildly (4)
2 Sacred river of India (6)
3 Relating to men (9)
4 Acquired money as profit (6)
6 Painter (6)
7 Curved surface of a liquid in a tube (8)
11 Incandescent lamp (9)
12 Study done to prepare for an event (8)
13 Cushion for the head (6)
14 Sporting venues (6)
15 Arachnid (6)
17 Woody plant (4)

CROSSWORD 141

Across

1 Diabolically cruel (8)
5 US pop star (4)
9 Gains possession of (5)
10 Seethed with anger (5)
11 Impenetrable (10)
14 Entice or attract (6)
15 Doing nothing (6)
17 Give emphasis to (10)
20 Reel for winding yarn (5)
21 Hurled away (5)
22 Cultivated (4)
23 Exclamation of surprise (8)

Down

1 Destiny (4)
2 Large deer (pl.) (4)
3 Hopelessly (12)
4 Small in degree (6)
6 Sanitary (8)
7 Plan anew (8)
8 Planned in advance (12)
12 Country in South East Asia (8)
13 Complete loss of electrical power (8)
16 A size of book page (6)
18 Correct; accurate (4)
19 Possesses (4)

Across

1 Move with short sharp turns (6)

7 Catering to high-income consumers (8)

8 Father (3)

9 Spanish festival (6)

10 Put down gently (4)

11 Shyly (5)

13 Slim (7)

15 Baffles (7)

17 Fills a suitcase (5)

21 Suggestion or tip (4)

22 Gallic (6)

23 Tree that bears acorns (3)

24 Giant ocean waves (8)

25 Walk very quietly (6)

Down

1 Group of 12 constellations (6)

2 Annoying person (6)

3 Estimate (5)

4 Friendly (7)

5 Formerly Ceylon (3,5)

6 Bring back to life (6)

12 Gets brighter (8)

14 Scent; smell (7)

16 Serving no functional purpose (6)

18 Roman military unit (6)

19 Farming tool (6)

20 Wild animal; monster (5)

CROSSWORD 143

Across

1 After the beginning of (4)
3 Mocking (8)
9 People who attack at speed (7)
10 Dried kernel of the coconut (5)
11 Toothed wheel (3)
12 Wide-awake (5)
13 Sheikhdom on the Persian Gulf (5)
15 Confess to (5)
17 Wanderer (5)
18 Range of knowledge (3)
19 Give a false notion of (5)
20 Below (7)
21 Publicity (8)
22 Stinging insect (4)

Down

1 Irretrievable (13)
2 Unspecified object (5)
4 State a belief confidently (6)
5 Formal announcements (12)
6 Brother's children (7)
7 Artisanship (13)
8 Main premises of a company (12)
14 Surround entirely (7)
16 One who belongs to a group (6)
18 Australian marsupial (5)

Across

1 Unit of length (4)
3 Explicit (8)
9 Dandier (anag.) (7)
10 Furnish with new weapons (5)
11 Relinquish (5)
12 Uncommon (7)
13 Disposition (6)
15 Respect and admire (6)
17 Seriously (7)
18 Sticky sap (5)
20 Puff up (5)
21 Country in West Africa (7)
22 Writer of literary works (8)
23 In a lazy way (4)

Down

1 Untiring (13)
2 Seat (5)
4 Lectern (6)
5 Restrict within limits (12)
6 Any part of the face (7)
7 Harmonious; compatible (13)
8 Incomprehensibly (12)
14 Pastures (7)
16 Rides a bike (6)
19 Very small amount (5)

CROSSWORD 145

Across

1 Cave in (8)

5 Freshwater game fish (4)

9 Place where something happens (5)

10 Reduce prices substantially (5)

11 Succeed or fail without external help (4,2,4)

14 Written document (6)

15 Irrelevant pieces of information (6)

17 Complete cessation of taking a drug (4,6)

20 Small tuned drum (5)

21 Semiconductor (5)

22 Golf pegs (4)

23 Reproduce recorded sound (4,4)

Down

1 Small sheltered bay (4)

2 Connect (4)

3 Improvement in a condition (12)

4 Leaf stems (6)

6 Period of unusually hot weather (4,4)

7 Unconventional person (8)

8 Intuitively designed (of a system) (4-8)

12 Highly critical remark (8)

13 Wealth (8)

16 Largest South American country (6)

18 Flaring star (4)

19 Look for (4)

Across

1 Spherical objects (6)
5 Designated limit (3,3)
8 Having little or no hair (4)
9 Mathematics of points and lines (8)
10 Jostle and push (5)
11 Binned (7)
14 Amusement park ride (6,7)
16 Small stones (7)
18 Looks good on (5)
20 Formal curse by a pope (8)
22 Violent disturbance (4)
23 Casual but stylish (of clothing) (6)
24 Neglect (6)

Down

2 Revolting (9)
3 Torment or harass (7)
4 Emit a breath of sadness (4)
5 Young male church singer (8)
6 Large woody plants (5)
7 Distant (3)
12 Subatomic particles (9)
13 Foliage (8)
15 Multiplies a number by itself (7)
17 Tribe (anag.) (5)
19 Beach constituent (4)
21 Short sleep (3)

CROSSWORD 147

Across

1 Electrically charged particles (4)
3 These come after afternoons (8)
9 State of being very poor (7)
10 Scale representation (5)
11 Tool for making holes in leather (3)
12 Research deeply (5)
13 Lance (5)
15 Cry of excitement (5)
17 Capital of Egypt (5)
18 Chain attached to a watch (3)
19 Utter impulsively (5)
20 Respectable; refined (7)
21 Improving the mind; enlightening (8)
22 Verge (4)

Down

1 Unfeasible (13)
2 What an author writes (5)
4 Journey by sea (6)
5 Practice of mentioning
  famous people one knows (4-8)
6 Small rounded lumps (7)
7 25th anniversary celebration (6,7)
8 Laudatory (12)
14 Things that evoke reactions (7)
16 Gas we breathe (6)
18 Released from jail (5)

Across

1 Person who supports a cause (8)
5 Large bag (4)
8 Levies; chimes (5)
9 Essentially (7)
10 Sweet course (7)
12 African country with capital Windhoek (7)
14 Precede in time (7)
16 Sharp tooth (7)
18 Damaging immune response (7)
19 Opposite one of two (5)
20 Deserve (4)
21 Fellow Christians (8)

Down

1 Singing voice (4)
2 Inert gaseous element (6)
3 Looks like (9)
4 State of the USA (6)
6 Not awake (6)
7 Central principle of a system (8)
11 Watercraft with a motor (9)
12 Propose a candidate for office (8)
13 Having only magnitude (of a quantity) (6)
14 Request made to God (6)
15 Heavy metal weight (6)
17 Smile broadly (4)

CROSSWORD 149

Across

1 Large bodies of water (4)
3 Someone who talks in a foolish way (8)
9 Becomes less severe (7)
10 Departing (5)
11 Opposite of old (3)
12 Tease or pester (5)
13 Make thirsty (5)
15 Possessor (5)
17 Embed; type of filling (5)
18 Saw (anag.) (3)
19 Cutting instrument (5)
20 Acquiescent (7)
21 Worm (8)
22 Bonus; positive (4)

Down

1 Young person (6,7)
2 Softly radiant (5)
4 Register of duties (6)
5 Fellowship (12)
6 Time off (7)
7 Virtuousness (13)
8 Joblessness (12)
14 Element with atomic number 31 (7)
16 Bit sharply (6)
18 Spin (5)

Across

1 Brushes (6)
5 Touch gently (3)
7 Sycophant (5)
8 Farm vehicle (7)
9 Criminal deception (5)
10 Messy and untidy (of appearance) (8)
12 Written agreement (6)
14 Makes fun of someone (6)
17 Grows more mature (8)
18 Microorganisms (5)
20 Expecting prices to fall (7)
21 Piquant (5)
22 Very small child (3)
23 Live in (6)

Down

2 Singer; type of bird (7)
3 People in hospital (8)
4 One of two equal parts (4)
5 Oppressive rulers (7)
6 Very fine substances (7)
7 Genuinely (5)
11 Emissary (8)
12 Line that touches a curve (7)
13 Put in someone's care (7)
15 Laid open to view (7)
16 Local sporting match (5)
19 Revolve around quickly (4)

Across

1 Flashing point on a radar screen (4)

3 Dowdiness (8)

9 Admit something is true (7)

10 Pointed projectile (5)

11 Firework display (12)

14 Close-fitting hat (3)

16 Shadow (5)

17 Cease (3)

18 Not intoxicating (of a drink) (12)

21 Corpulent (5)

22 Pipe (7)

23 Bookish (8)

24 Charges (4)

Down

1 Rucksack (8)

2 Interior (5)

4 Cereal grass (3)

5 Forcible indoctrination (12)

6 Aural pain (7)

7 Fastened with stitches (4)

8 The proprietor of an eating establishment (12)

12 Having three dimensions (5)

13 Teaches (8)

15 Keep safe from harm (7)

19 Ousel (anag.) (5)

20 Ring a bell (4)

22 Snappy dog (3)

CROSSWORD 152

Across

7 Crucial (8)

8 Gentle accent (4)

9 First son of Adam and Eve (4)

10 A sound defeat (8)

11 Deserved (7)

12 Concise and full of meaning (5)

15 Pulls along forcefully (5)

17 Uppermost layer of something (7)

20 Noble title (8)

22 Fleet of ships (4)

23 Retain (4)

24 Float in the air (8)

Down

1 Elaborately adorned (6)

2 Foul-smelling (8)

3 Sped along; skimmed (7)

4 E.g. cumulus (5)

5 Amorphous shape (4)

6 Wince (6)

13 Unending (8)

14 Sly (7)

16 Attacked at speed (6)

18 Decayed part of a tooth (6)

19 Not straight (of hair) (5)

21 Headland (4)

CROSSWORD 153

Across

1 Competition stages (6)
4 Paler (6)
9 Useful (7)
10 Have a positive impact on (7)
11 Rescuer (5)
12 Survived (5)
14 Entrance hall (5)
15 Not clearly stated (5)
17 E.g. square or circle (5)
18 Make less dark (7)
20 Strong desire for a thing (7)
21 Most secure (6)
22 Deceives; finest (anag.) (6)

Down

1 Recycle old material (6)
2 Not giving affection (8)
3 Postpone (5)
5 Contentedly (7)
6 Very large book (4)
7 Awakened (6)
8 Symbol of reconciliation (5,6)
13 Annoyance (8)
14 Subatomic particles such as electrons (7)
15 Personal attendants (6)
16 Equine sounds (6)
17 Satisfy a thirst (5)
19 Sea inlet (4)

Across

1 Morals (6)

7 Stop gradually (5,3)

8 Pear-shaped fruit (3)

9 Stashes away (6)

10 Story (4)

11 Linear measures of three feet (5)

13 Reserved (7)

15 Superficial (7)

17 Fail to reach the required standard in an exam (5)

21 Mace (anag.) (4)

22 Sea in northern Europe (6)

23 Limb used for walking (3)

24 Captive (8)

25 Adjust in advance of its use (6)

Down

1 Representation of a person (6)

2 Opposite of lower (6)

3 Part of a church tower (5)

4 Small plum-like fruits (7)

5 Pertaining to the chest (8)

6 Make illegal (6)

12 Distribute (8)

14 Swimming aid (7)

16 Straighten out (6)

18 Male relatives (6)

19 Chess piece (6)

20 Drink noisily (5)

Across

1 Face (anag.) (4)
3 Wristband (8)
9 Newness (7)
10 Unpleasant giants (5)
11 Branch of astronomy (12)
13 Hold a position or job (6)
15 Lump or blob (6)
17 Uneasy (12)
20 Skewered meat (5)
21 Grazed (7)
22 Feigns (8)
23 Medium-sized feline (4)

Down

1 Spice (8)
2 One side of a gem (5)
4 Sense of musical time (6)
5 Long race (5-7)
6 Expressive (of music) (7)
7 Elephant tooth (4)
8 Without equal (12)
12 Supplemental part of a book (8)
14 Competent (7)
16 Done in stages (6)
18 State indirectly (5)
19 Bypass (4)

Across

1 Spur on (4)
3 Commotion (8)
9 Visual symbolism (7)
10 Kind of wheat (5)
11 Nip (anag.) (3)
12 Torn apart (5)
13 Vertical spars for sails (5)
15 Underwater breathing device (5)
17 Follow stealthily (5)
18 For each (3)
19 Fire (5)
20 E.g. iron or oxygen (7)
21 Person sent on a special mission (8)
22 Cry of derision (4)

Down

1 Totally trustworthy (13)
2 Speck of food (5)
4 Poems; sounds alike (6)
5 Inadequately manned (12)
6 Reached a destination (7)
7 Person who manages the affairs of an insolvent company (13)
8 Female school boss (12)
14 Type of natural disaster (7)
16 Raise up (6)
18 Part of (5)

CROSSWORD 157

Across

1 Perilously (11)
9 Accumulate (5)
10 Possess (3)
11 Large fruit with pulpy flesh (5)
12 Belonging to them (5)
13 Money given generously (8)
16 Timetable (8)
18 Greek writer of fables (5)
21 Implied (5)
22 Measure of length (3)
23 Nationality of Oscar Wilde (5)
24 Compose a dance routine (11)

Down

2 Fishermen (7)
3 Recipient of funding (7)
4 Domains (6)
5 Surprise result (5)
6 Relaxed; not tense (5)
7 Difficult and intricate (11)
8 Increasing gradually by degrees (11)
14 Therein (anag.) (7)
15 The exposure of bedrock (7)
17 Building for gambling (6)
19 Graceful young woman (5)
20 Earlier (5)

Across

7 Person who prices things (6)

8 Start a fire (6)

9 Clothed (4)

10 Outlines in detail (8)

11 Policeman or woman (7)

13 Not taut (5)

15 Sheep sound (5)

16 Light beard (7)

18 Device that tests for the presence of something (8)

19 Rules of a country (4)

21 Renovate (6)

22 Disliking intensely (6)

Down

1 Scoop water out of a boat (4)

2 Four-sided figure (13)

3 Better for the environment (7)

4 Leaps over a rope (5)

5 State of being unable to err (13)

6 Coldly detached (8)

12 Started to lose strength (8)

14 Stiff and formal (7)

17 Halts (5)

20 Alcoholic beverage (4)

CROSSWORD 159

Across

7 Liar (8)

8 Circuits of a racetrack (4)

9 Reveal indiscreetly (4)

10 Saddled with a heavy load (8)

11 Addresses boldly (7)

12 Refine metal (5)

15 Small (5)

17 Origins (7)

20 Expulsion (8)

22 Knocks lightly (4)

23 Boast (4)

24 Fanaticism (8)

Down

1 Characteristically French (6)

2 Protective skin cream (8)

3 Communal settlement in Israel (7)

4 Large wading bird (5)

5 Smoke passage (4)

6 Be attractive (6)

13 Long foot race (8)

14 Coarsen (anag.) (7)

16 Physical wound (6)

18 End of the period when something is valid (6)

19 Giddy (5)

21 Gear wheels (4)

Across

1 Large bodies of water (6)
5 Raise in relief (6)
8 Obstacle (4)
9 Innate ability (8)
10 Fragile (5)
11 Misfortune (3,4)
14 Eternally (13)
16 Inflexible and unyielding (7)
18 Remove paint from a wall (5)
20 Aromatic shrub (8)
22 Protruding part of the lower jaw (4)
23 Capital of New South Wales (6)
24 Bearlike (6)

Down

2 Artificial; deliberately made (9)
3 More irate (7)
4 Move from side to side (4)
5 Competition participants (8)
6 Asian pepper plant (5)
7 Sorrowful (3)
12 Crash (9)
13 In a refined manner (8)
15 Announcements (7)
17 Craftsman who uses stone (5)
19 Boyfriend or male admirer (4)
21 Put down (3)

CROSSWORD 161

Across

1 Drains of energy (4)
3 Suggesting (8)
9 Well balanced (of character) (7)
10 Appear suddenly (3,2)
11 Absurd (12)
14 Climbing vine (3)
16 Accustom (5)
17 Water barrier (3)
18 Pertaining to letters (12)
21 Higher than (5)
22 Act of preparing food (7)
23 Waver (8)
24 Lies (anag.) (4)

Down

1 Angel of the highest order (8)
2 Long cloud of smoke (5)
4 Not new (3)
5 Flaw (12)
6 Seize and take custody of (7)
7 Spaces or intervals (4)
8 Firm rebuke (12)
12 Pollex (5)
13 Worker (8)
15 E.g. primrose and lemon (7)
19 Cooks (5)
20 Money in notes or coins (4)
22 Bed for a baby or for camping (3)

Across

1 Someone who writes the words for a song (8)

5 Business (4)

9 Underground worker (5)

10 Long pointed elephant teeth (5)

11 Hall or seating area (10)

14 Juicy citrus fruit (6)

15 Concurs (6)

17 Large city (10)

20 Legal process (5)

21 Arboreal primate (5)

22 Unpleasant smell (4)

23 Extravagant (8)

Down

1 E.g. an arm or leg (4)

2 Skating venue (4)

3 Brusque and surly (12)

4 Stress; pull a muscle (6)

6 Made another excited about (8)

7 Confused mixture (8)

8 Determined (6-6)

12 One who travels to work regularly (8)

13 Type of employment (4-4)

16 Red dog (anag.) (6)

18 Type of air pollution (4)

19 Spoken exam (4)

CROSSWORD 163

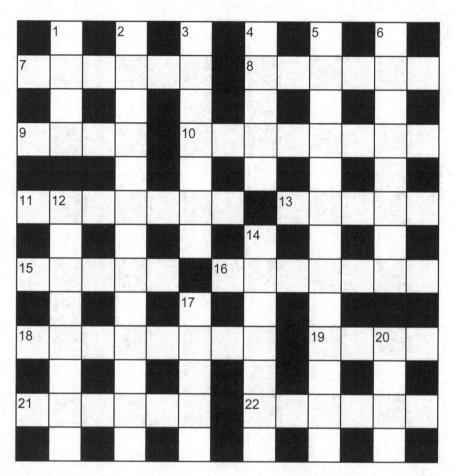

Across

7 Lender (6)
8 Commercial aircraft (6)
9 Plant used to make linen (4)
10 E.g. Baz Luhrmann (8)
11 Arid areas (7)
13 Hand shovel (5)
15 Moist (of air) (5)
16 Items made from fired clay (7)
18 Hurting; throbbing (8)
19 Period of imprisonment (4)
21 Secret (6)
22 Bowed string instruments (6)

Down

1 Get the opinions of people (4)
2 Wet behind the ears (13)
3 Learned (7)
4 Exhibitions (5)
5 E.g. rain or snow (13)
6 Taxonomic group (8)
12 Explosion (8)
14 Absolve (7)
17 Grimy (5)
20 Quantity of paper (4)

Across

1 Gangs (4)

3 Type of Eurasian carp (8)

9 Pertaining to the stars (7)

10 E.g. copper or calcium (5)

11 Gregarious deer (3)

12 Compass point (5)

13 TV presenters (5)

15 Moderate and well-balanced (5)

17 Insect larva (5)

18 Large vessel (3)

19 Fish-eating mammal (5)

20 Swollen (7)

21 Building examiner (8)

22 Pottery material (4)

Down

1 Of mixed character (13)

2 Desolate (5)

4 Female monster (6)

5 One who takes part in a protest (12)

6 Time between events (7)

7 Unenthusiastically (4-9)

8 Framework for washed garments (7,5)

14 Device that measures electric current (7)

16 Treelike grass (6)

18 Essential (5)

CROSSWORD 165

Across

1 Select (6)
5 Mock (3)
7 Powerful forward movement (5)
8 Stimulate a reaction (7)
9 Covers with gold (5)
10 Come to an end (8)
12 A complex whole (6)
14 Boundary (6)
17 Comment at the bottom of a page (8)
18 Act of stealing (5)
20 Restless (7)
21 Assists in a crime (5)
22 Your (poetic) (3)
23 Was scared of (6)

Down

2 Accord (7)
3 Take responsibility for (8)
4 Tailless amphibian (4)
5 Retorted (7)
6 Rocket stage giving initial acceleration (7)
7 Transmits (5)
11 Fashion shop (8)
12 Least hard (7)
13 At an unspecified future time (7)
15 Exceptional; not usual (7)
16 Concentrate on (5)
19 Arduous journey (4)

Across

1 Shallow dish (6)
5 Repudiate (6)
8 Number after three (4)
9 Drink (8)
10 Small garden statue (5)
11 Stored away (7)
14 Disreputable (13)
16 In a nimble manner (7)
18 Bucks (5)
20 Bulbous perennial herb (8)
22 Microscopic arachnid (4)
23 Country in North Europe (6)
24 Document granting invention rights (6)

Down

2 Teeming (9)
3 Made of clay hardened by heat (7)
4 Loose flowing garment (4)
5 Fit together easily (8)
6 Rides the waves (5)
7 Swish (of an animal's tail) (3)
12 Illuminate (9)
13 Sheets and pillowcases (8)
15 Try (7)
17 Expressed clearly (5)
19 Vessel (4)
21 Coniferous tree (3)

CROSSWORD 167

Across

1 Pulsates (6)
5 Cooking utensil (3)
7 Benefactor (5)
8 Split (7)
9 Informs (5)
10 Scrawl (8)
12 Speaks (6)
14 Assent or agree to (6)
17 Straddle (8)
18 Loose scrums (rugby) (5)
20 Hauled (7)
21 Gives temporarily (5)
22 Not wet (3)
23 Season of the Church year (6)

Down

2 Coiffure (7)
3 Small North American avian (8)
4 Midge (4)
5 Introductory piece of music (7)
6 Shaving of the crown of head (7)
7 Leads (anag.) (5)
11 Where one finds Glasgow (8)
12 Not carrying weapons (7)
13 Densely (7)
15 Feeling of indignation (7)
16 Rushes (5)
19 Transmit (4)

Across

1 Mission (4)

3 Person who advocates change (8)

9 Early part of the day (7)

10 Ceases trading (5)

11 Intricate and confusing (12)

13 Rough drawing (6)

15 Edge (6)

17 Insistently (12)

20 A central point (5)

21 Act of reading carefully (7)

22 Base of a statue (8)

23 Wipes up (4)

Down

1 Eternal (8)

2 Small woody plant (5)

4 Machine that produces motion (6)

5 Unofficially (3,3,6)

6 Dark pigment in skin (7)

7 Fragrant flower (4)

8 Type of cloud (12)

12 Uses again (8)

14 Changed gradually (7)

16 Ideally perfect state (6)

18 Rope with a running noose (5)

19 Break suddenly (4)

CROSSWORD 169

Across

1 Landmarks; spectacles (6)
4 Enclosed recess (6)
9 Prescription (7)
10 Becomes established in a new place (7)
11 Stringed instruments (5)
12 Finicky (5)
14 Small motor-racing vehicles (5)
15 Flinch away in pain (5)
17 Chopped finely (5)
18 Go back over again (7)
20 West Indian musical style (7)
21 Third sign of the zodiac (6)
22 Dried grape (6)

Down

1 Securely (6)
2 Whirling motion (8)
3 Routs (anag.) (5)
5 Portable computers (7)
6 Close securely; aquatic mammal (4)
7 Of inferior quality (6)
8 An example of great artistry (11)
13 Abstract ideas (8)
14 Protein found in hair (7)
15 System of cables (6)
16 Border (6)
17 Triangular river mouth (5)
19 Neat in appearance (4)

Across

7 In a cagey manner (13)
8 Uncertain if God exists (8)
9 Engrossed (4)
10 Rainy season (7)
12 Impertinence (5)
14 Plant stalks (5)
16 These follow Sundays (7)
19 Suddenly reject; walk out on (4)
20 Popular places (8)
22 Presentation on how to use something (13)

Down

1 Make musical sounds (4)
2 Sound reflections (6)
3 E.g. hate or joy (7)
4 Small spot (5)
5 Sear (6)
6 Unreliable; shifty (8)
11 Gave a summary of (8)
13 Stands about idly (7)
15 Sheep meat (6)
17 Person who acts for another (6)
18 Stage (5)
21 Snatched (4)

CROSSWORD 171

Across

1 Debilitated (8)

5 Snare (4)

8 Lubricated (5)

9 Become rigid (7)

10 Official language of Britain (7)

12 Alfresco (4-3)

14 Performer of gymnastic feats (7)

16 Flat slabs (7)

18 Final stage of an extended
   process (7)

19 Name of a book (5)

20 Throw a coin in the air (4)

21 Respected and admired (8)

Down

1 Dense growth of trees (4)

2 On fire (6)

3 Stamina (9)

4 Simpler (6)

6 A palm tree (6)

7 Strong inclination (8)

11 Promise with certainty (9)

12 Salve (8)

13 Dwells in (6)

14 Items of value (6)

15 Small chicken (6)

17 Large group of cattle (4)

Across

1 Delightfully (11)
9 Complete trust (5)
10 Interdict (3)
11 Alert (5)
12 Garners (5)
13 Enthusiasm (8)
16 Ballroom dance (8)
18 Soothes (5)
21 Take illegally (5)
22 Fishing pole (3)
23 Smallest quantity (5)
24 Going on and on (5-6)

Down

2 Pledged to marry (7)
3 Raging fire (7)
4 Iridaceous plants (6)
5 Law court official (5)
6 Sign of the zodiac (5)
7 Past performances (5,6)
8 Plant-eating insect (11)
14 Attributed to (7)
15 Brutal; cruel (7)
17 Place where something is set (6)
19 Ridge (5)
20 Find the solution (5)

CROSSWORD 173

Across

1 Extraterrestrial objects (6)
7 Make beautiful (8)
8 Small truck (3)
9 Arrive (4,2)
10 Snooker players use these (4)
11 State of disgrace (5)
13 Predatory fish (7)
15 Motor-driven revolving cylinder (7)
17 Chunk (5)
21 Mythical creature (4)
22 Increase in intensity (4,2)
23 Be in debt (3)
24 Fighter in close combat (8)
25 Be contingent upon (6)

Down

1 Conceals with a cloth (6)
2 Vedic hymn (6)
3 Pay out money (5)
4 Plunder (7)
5 Enclosure formed from upright stakes (8)
6 Anew (6)
12 Uses seam (anag.) (8)
14 Adornments of hanging threads (7)
16 Long-haired variety of cat (6)
18 Remove from office (6)
19 Surpass (6)
20 Facial hair (5)

Across

7 Extremely alarming (5-8)

8 Surroundings (8)

9 Solicit custom (4)

10 Acts in a disloyal manner (7)

12 Overcomes (5)

14 Boxes lightly (5)

16 Snake (7)

19 SI unit of electromotive force (4)

20 Desires; cravings (8)

22 Serving to show (13)

Down

1 Narrow valley (4)

2 Duplicating machine (6)

3 Kind of abbreviation (7)

4 Squeeze (5)

5 Happy; carefree (6)

6 Undo a shirt (8)

11 Blew up (8)

13 Having three sections (7)

15 Sat an exam again (6)

17 Statue base (6)

18 Dental care item (5)

21 Hand over (4)

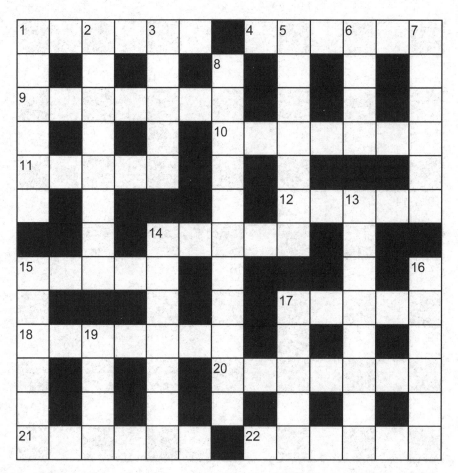

Across

1 Multiply by two (6)
4 Given out (6)
9 Luggage (7)
10 Formally approved (7)
11 Household garbage (5)
12 Discourage (5)
14 Concealing garments (5)
15 Group of activists (5)
17 Strong lightweight wood (5)
18 Close to the shore (7)
20 In a relaxed manner (7)
21 Protects from heat (6)
22 Not so important (6)

Down

1 Bedsit (anag.) (6)
2 Improved equipment (8)
3 Drain away from soil (of a chemical) (5)
5 Disguises or covers (7)
6 An individual thing (4)
7 Totter or tremble (6)
8 Wonderfully (11)
13 Loftiness (8)
14 Risky enterprise (7)
15 Hidden storage places (6)
16 Legal practitioner (6)
17 Ruined; rendered inoperable (5)
19 Distinctive atmosphere created by a person (4)

Across

1 Passage (4)

3 Moral instructions (8)

9 Move in an exaggerated manner (7)

10 Ranked (5)

11 Despicable (12)

14 Not in (3)

16 Evil spirit (5)

17 Commotion (3)

18 Relating to horoscopes (12)

21 Garbage or drivel (5)

22 Waterfall (7)

23 Very small unit of length (8)

24 Topical information (4)

Down

1 Deserter (8)

2 Children's entertainer (5)

4 Fish eggs (3)

5 Heart specialist (12)

6 Kneecap (7)

7 Froth of soap and water (4)

8 Clothing such as a vest (12)

12 Go about stealthily (5)

13 Calmness under pressure (8)

15 Throwing a coin in the air (7)

19 Pursue in order to catch (5)

20 Volcano in Sicily (4)

22 Dove sound (3)

Across

1 Of the universe (6)

7 Person in second place (6-2)

8 Wetland (3)

9 Feeling of resentment (6)

10 Opposite of thick (4)

11 Staggers (5)

13 Moved off course (7)

15 Have within (7)

17 Minor road (5)

21 One more than four (4)

22 Ruler (6)

23 Wet soil (3)

24 Remove from action (8)

25 Hesitate (6)

Down

1 Strongbox for valuables (6)

2 Solitary (6)

3 Coarse (5)

4 Friendly understanding (7)

5 Third in order (8)

6 Lying on the back (6)

12 Formally educated (8)

14 Choice cut of beef (7)

16 Egyptian god (6)

18 Heat; affection (6)

19 Over there (6)

20 Rescued (5)

Across

1 Soldiers (6)
4 Begin to grow (6)
9 Expect; suppose to be true (7)
10 Stinging plants (7)
11 Paces (5)
12 Conventions (5)
14 Hankered after (5)
15 Sequence (5)
17 Device that splits light (5)
18 A child beginning to walk (7)
20 Unity (7)
21 Tropical fruit (6)
22 Relative social standing (6)

Down

1 Computer keyboard user (6)
2 Small-scale musical drama (8)
3 Pulls a sulky face (5)
5 Imaginary (7)
6 Egg-shaped (4)
7 Throws a coin in the air (6)
8 Solid figure with five faces (11)
13 Reserved; diffident (8)
14 Comparison (7)
15 Doze (6)
16 Entertains (6)
17 Double fold in a garment (5)
19 Let fall (4)

Across

1 Level and regular (4)
3 Clamber (8)
9 Iron lever (7)
10 Supple (5)
11 Make a guess that is too high (12)
14 Bashful; reluctant to give details (3)
16 Singing voice (5)
17 Cry of disapproval (3)
18 In a creative manner (12)
21 Detected a sound (5)
22 Slender stemlike plant appendage (7)
23 Short account of an incident (8)
24 Close (4)

Down

1 Make gradual inroads (8)
2 Call forth (5)
4 Four-wheeled road vehicle (3)
5 Comprehensive (3-9)
6 Large household water container (7)
7 At any time (4)
8 Lost in thought (6-6)
12 Religious doctrine (5)
13 Speaking many languages (8)
15 Golfing measure of distance (7)
19 Stagger (5)
20 Ostrich-like bird (4)
22 Exclamation of contempt (3)

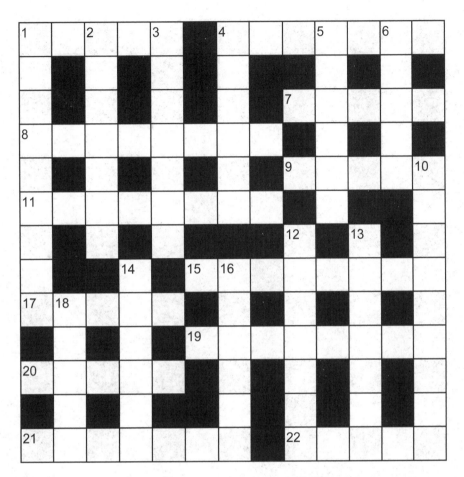

Across

1 Mountain range in South America (5)

4 Heart-shaped (7)

7 Slithering animal (5)

8 Facing (8)

9 Sink; sag (5)

11 Substance that nourishes (8)

15 Written guarantee (8)

17 Climb (5)

19 Disloyal person (8)

20 Crunch; wear down (5)

21 Able to read minds (7)

22 Contest (5)

Down

1 Detachment (9)

2 Dictators (7)

3 Of enormous effect (7)

4 Small territorial district (6)

5 Benefactors (6)

6 Capital of Japan (5)

10 Lie detector (9)

12 Liberty (7)

13 A precise point in time (7)

14 Medical treatment place (6)

16 Pertaining to vinegar (6)

18 Races (anag.) (5)

CROSSWORD 181

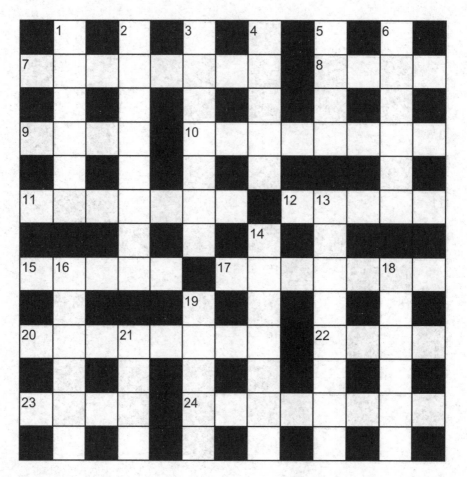

Across

7 Association created for mutual benefit (8)
8 Extol (4)
9 Witty remark (4)
10 Relating to critical explanation (8)
11 Enlist (7)
12 Begin (5)
15 Temporary stop (5)
17 Worry (7)
20 In a carefree manner (8)
22 Ripped (4)
23 Device sounding a warning (4)
24 White flakes in the hair (8)

Down

1 Refer to indirectly (6)
2 E.g. Heathrow and Gatwick (8)
3 Acquire as an heir (7)
4 Divide by cutting (5)
5 Hint (4)
6 More active (6)
13 Not inclined to talk (8)
14 Imitating (7)
16 Covered in flowers (6)
18 Make less dense (6)
19 Small decorative balls (5)
21 Look after (4)

Across

7 Scarcity (6)
8 Made amends for (6)
9 Scheme (4)
10 Defamed (8)
11 Coming first (7)
13 Get on an aircraft (5)
15 Poison (5)
16 Stylishly (7)
18 By hand (8)
19 Bunch of threads (4)
21 Tremulous sounds (6)
22 Decreased one's speed (6)

Down

1 Transaction (4)
2 Affectedly (13)
3 Removing hair (7)
4 Buckets (5)
5 Hostile disagreement (13)
6 Intellectual (8)
12 Great adulation (8)
14 Infantile (7)
17 Surface shine (5)
20 Enemies (4)

CROSSWORD 183

Across

1 Dialect of a region (6)
5 Place (3)
7 Hard close-grained wood (5)
8 Reconstruct (7)
9 Longed for (5)
10 Suppressing (8)
12 Border (6)
14 Relays (anag.) (6)
17 Thoroughly conversant with (8)
18 Visual perception (5)
20 Large orange gourd (7)
21 Sufficiently (5)
22 Athletic facility (3)
23 Fillings (6)

Down

2 Prevented (7)
3 Habitually lazy (8)
4 Support (4)
5 Unit of sound in a language (7)
6 Bands of connective tissue (7)
7 Having nothing written on (of paper) (5)
11 Charm (8)
12 Deleting (7)
13 Cotton fabric (7)
15 The world as it is (7)
16 Content (5)
19 Hints (4)

Across

1 Draw into the mouth using a straw (4)
3 Financially ruined (8)
9 Cleaned its feathers (of a bird) (7)
10 Looks slyly (5)
11 Expressing emotions (of poetry) (5)
12 Print anew (7)
13 Fictional (4,2)
15 Scottish sheep dog (6)
17 Makes ineffective (7)
18 Converses casually (5)
20 Warning sound (5)
21 Make better (7)
22 Submissive (8)
23 Snake-like fish (4)

Down

1 Additional (13)
2 Lucid (5)
4 Venomous snakes (6)
5 Children's toy (12)
6 Object used in the kitchen (7)
7 Blandness (13)
8 Not familiar with or used to (12)
14 Break down chemically (7)
16 Mete out (6)
19 Positively charged electrode (5)

CROSSWORD 185

Across

1 Moves very slowly (6)
5 Metal container; element (3)
7 Small and round and shiny (5)
8 One who finds water by dowsing (7)
9 Establish as the truth (5)
10 New World quail (8)
12 Renounce (6)
14 Gaudy (6)
17 Group of spectators (8)
18 Injures (5)
20 Pertaining to a river (7)
21 Pools (anag.) (5)
22 Beam of light (3)
23 Weirder; more uncanny (6)

Down

2 Horizontal plant stem (7)
3 Hitting with the fist (8)
4 Inclined plane (4)
5 Wealthy businesspeople (7)
6 Flower arrangement (7)
7 Scamps (5)
11 Height (8)
12 Earthquake scale (7)
13 Refined; polite (7)
15 Unit of square measure (7)
16 Swells (5)
19 Drive away (4)

Across

7 Spend time in an inactive way (8)

8 Long bounding stride (4)

9 Get beaten (4)

10 Gives a right to (8)

11 Come out on top (7)

12 Strange (5)

15 Group of students; category (5)

17 Horizontal supporting beams (7)

20 Defeat (8)

22 Status (4)

23 Shoe with a wooden sole (4)

24 Inclined (8)

Down

1 Eat hungrily; gobble (6)

2 Gets given (8)

3 Spear thrown in athletics (7)

4 Small pier (5)

5 Move rapidly (4)

6 Seem (6)

13 Coming from outside (8)

14 Varied (7)

16 Floors of a building (6)

18 Yearned for (6)

19 Verbose (5)

21 Intense anger (4)

Across

1 Fine powder (4)
3 Believable; plausible (8)
9 Part of a room opposite the floor (7)
10 Break the rules (5)
11 Conjuring trick (5)
12 Device that records the movements of someone (7)
13 Expelled from office (6)
15 Part of the eye (6)
17 Slanted letters (7)
18 Beauty shop (5)
20 Arm of a body of water (5)
21 Copy; mimic (7)
22 Recently married (5-3)
23 Encounter; come across (4)

Down

1 Decay (13)
2 Move back and forth (5)
4 Legal entitlements (6)
5 Absolute authority in any sphere (12)
6 Type of robbery (5-2)
7 Amusement (13)
8 Science of biological processes (12)
14 Swift-flying songbird (7)
16 Aim to achieve something (6)
19 Let (5)

Across

1 Able to adjust (8)
5 Soothing ointment (4)
8 Titled (5)
9 Very young infant (7)
10 Severe mental suffering (7)
12 Corridor (7)
14 Tidal mouth of a river (7)
16 Natural series of changes (7)
18 Country in West Africa (7)
19 Snarl (5)
20 Be foolishly fond of (4)
21 Gathering (8)

Down

1 Skin condition on the face (4)
2 Quantity you can hold (6)
3 Tsunami (5,4)
4 Conceit (6)
6 Openly declared (6)
7 Lack of variety (8)
11 Shape with four straight sides (9)
12 Occurred (8)
13 Struggled against (6)
14 Pieces of writing (6)
15 Boards (anag.) (6)
17 Ruse (4)

CROSSWORD 189

Across

1 Broadest (6)
5 Unit of resistance (3)
7 Steep slope (5)
8 Ragtime (anag.) (7)
9 Military constructions (5)
10 Went along to an event (8)
12 Hurting (6)
14 Individual (6)
17 Carve words on something (8)
18 Hushed (5)
20 Draws forth (7)
21 Chessmen (5)
22 Animal fodder (3)
23 Gastropods with shells (6)

Down

2 Stupid (7)
3 Having no current (of a body of water) (8)
4 Young cow (4)
5 Weigh down (7)
6 Make damp (7)
7 Number of deadly sins (5)
11 Response (8)
12 Horizontal angle of a compass bearing (7)
13 Study of the past (7)
15 Passing around a town (of a road) (7)
16 Leg joints (5)
19 Sailing vessel (4)

Across

1 Pretty (4)

3 Creative (8)

9 Apprehensive (7)

10 Connection; link (3-2)

11 Uncooked (of meat) (3)

12 The Norwegian language (5)

13 Solemn promises (5)

15 Brief smell (5)

17 Forgo; relinquish (5)

18 Increase in amount (3)

19 Tycoon (5)

20 Open air controlled blaze (7)

21 Opposite of southern (8)

22 Writing instruments (4)

Down

1 US female politician (13)

2 Hurl (5)

4 Place that is frequented for holidays (6)

5 Growing stronger (12)

6 A general proposition (7)

7 Satisfaction (13)

8 A grouping of states (12)

14 Sharp painful blow (7)

16 Line of equal pressure on a map (6)

18 Aimed (anag.) (5)

Across

1 Mischievous (6)
5 Sphere or globe (3)
7 Ape (abbrev.) (5)
8 Great suffering (7)
9 Shire (anag.) (5)
10 Process of becoming wider or more open (8)
12 Uncover (6)
14 Actually (6)
17 About to take place (8)
18 Water lily (5)
20 Lock of curly hair (7)
21 Correct (5)
22 Young goat (3)
23 Floor of a fireplace (6)

Down

2 Specify by name (7)
3 Playful (8)
4 Aquatic vertebrate (4)
5 Relating to sight (7)
6 Financial award (7)
7 Mayhem (5)
11 Repudiate (8)
12 Remove an obstruction (7)
13 Hot-tasting condiment (7)
15 Not strict (7)
16 Recreational activity (5)
19 Wise man (4)

Across

1 Person who hears (8)
5 Stop up a hole (4)
8 Meal (5)
9 Garden flower (7)
10 Retorts (7)
12 Prompting device (7)
14 Container releasing a fine spray (7)
16 Banners or flags (7)
18 Erased (7)
19 Awry; wrong (5)
20 Barriers to hold back water (4)
21 Evaluator (8)

Down

1 Hang loosely; droop (4)
2 Naturally illuminated (6)
3 Improving (9)
4 Cease to be valid (6)
6 Edible pulse (6)
7 Full measure of a drink (8)
11 Support of customers (9)
12 Climbed (8)
13 Shelter; place of refuge (6)
14 Stage whispers (6)
15 Cooks in wood chippings (6)
17 Pitcher (4)

Across

1 Lessens (6)

5 Damp (3)

7 Lucky accident (5)

8 Water-bearing rock (7)

9 Sailing ship (5)

10 Bliss (8)

12 Seek to hurt (6)

14 Woman in charge of nursing (6)

17 E.g. gels and emulsions (8)

18 Vends (5)

20 Mendicants (7)

21 Animal noise (5)

22 Be nosy (3)

23 Not moving or shaking (6)

Down

2 Legacy (7)

3 Ability to produce a desired result (8)

4 Style of popular dance music (4)

5 Atmospheric phenomenon (7)

6 Tropical cyclone (7)

7 Foam (5)

11 Small window (8)

12 Zeppelin (7)

13 Group of three plays (7)

15 Commanded (7)

16 Uncertainty (5)

19 Keep away from (4)

Across

7 One with extremely high standards (13)

8 Navigating (8)

9 Ditch filled with water (4)

10 Passionate (7)

12 Grows weary (5)

14 Very unpleasant (5)

16 Tragedy by Shakespeare (7)

19 Tablet (4)

20 Firmly establish (8)

22 Reach the required standard (3,3,7)

Down

1 Opening for air; outlet (4)

2 Special ___ : film illusion (6)

3 Accomplish (7)

4 Male monarchs (5)

5 Type of living organism (6)

6 Edible snail (8)

11 Compassionate (8)

13 Arrogance; loftiness (7)

15 Breaks apart forcibly (6)

17 Inhalation or exhalation of air (6)

18 Round cap (5)

21 Bend or coil (4)

Across

7 Unorthodox person (8)
8 Entice (4)
9 Bad habit (4)
10 Forbearance (8)
11 Sculpting (7)
12 Consecrate (5)
15 Skin marks from wounds (5)
17 Eventually (7)
20 Provided (8)
22 Fastened; suspended (4)
23 Brass instrument (4)
24 Unwelcome (8)

Down

1 Dock for small yachts (6)
2 Trickster (8)
3 Giving money in recognition of good service (7)
4 Comedy performances (5)
5 Sheet of floating ice (4)
6 Vestiges (6)
13 Hating (8)
14 Take a seat (3,4)
16 Political meeting (6)
18 Hang around (6)
19 Passageway of the nose (5)
21 Ring (4)

Across

1 A system of measurement (6)
5 Permits (6)
8 Stick with a hook (4)
9 Swollen with fat (8)
10 Wander off track (5)
11 Confusing (7)
14 Documentation (13)
16 Overly conceited and arrogant (5-2)
18 Subatomic particle such as a photon (5)
20 Rude (8)
22 Cut of beef from the leg (4)
23 Bandage (6)
24 Internet sites where users can post comments (6)

Down

2 Law that is passed (9)
3 Deflect light (7)
4 Young lions (4)
5 Artificial water channel (8)
6 Name applied to something (5)
7 State of armed conflict (3)
12 New word or phrase (9)
13 Overflowing with praise (8)
15 Routers (anag.) (7)
17 Hit hard (5)
19 Part of a plant (4)
21 Cut grass (3)

CROSSWORD 197

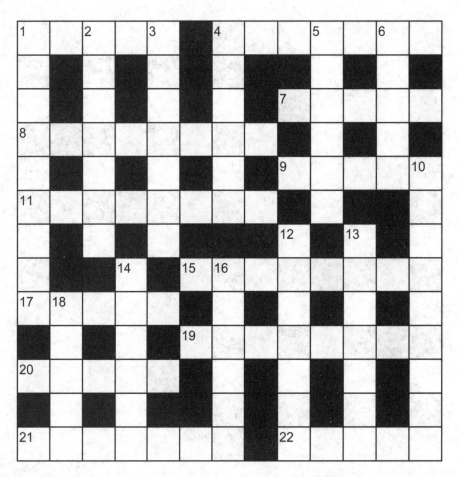

Across

1 Waggish (5)
4 Country in South America (7)
7 Under (5)
8 Taking away (8)
9 Express one's opinion (5)
11 Unusual (8)
15 A desert in south-western Africa (8)
17 Very foolish (5)
19 Cocktail (8)
20 Annoys (5)
21 Receptacle for cigarette residue (7)
22 Royal (5)

Down

1 Reduced (9)
2 Remnant (7)
3 Reveals (anag.) (7)
4 Republic once ruled by Idi Amin (6)
5 Hotel patrons (6)
6 High up (5)
10 Derived from experience (9)
12 Varnish (7)
13 Moving along the ground (of aircraft) (7)
14 Imperfection (6)
16 Absence of passion or interest (6)
18 Removes the lid (5)

Across

1 Most jolly (8)
5 Upper front part of a boot (4)
9 Style of Greek architecture (5)
10 Arose from slumber (5)
11 Victorious (10)
14 Set of clothes (6)
15 Getting older (6)
17 Able to be ended (10)
20 Tortoise carapace (5)
21 Identical copy (5)
22 Dispatched (4)
23 Exterior of a motor vehicle (8)

Down

1 Method; fashion (4)
2 Uncommon (4)
3 Incurably bad (12)
4 Reactive metal (6)
6 Having a strong smell (8)
7 Repute; standing (8)
8 Carefree (5-2-5)
12 Competitions (8)
13 Large fish (8)
16 Small summer-house (6)
18 Performance by one actor (4)
19 Abrupt movement (4)

CROSSWORD 199

Across

7 Witty reply (8)

8 Jump (4)

9 Of like kind (4)

10 Defer (8)

11 Measured heaviness (7)

12 Purple fruits (5)

15 Barely sufficient (5)

17 Capital of Northern Ireland (7)

20 Comfy seat (8)

22 Direct one's gaze (4)

23 Rage (anag.) (4)

24 Of striking appropriateness (8)

Down

1 Work out logically (6)

2 Disease-producing agent (8)

3 Stood on another's foot (7)

4 Microscopic fungus (5)

5 Fail totally (4)

6 Large wine bottle (6)

13 Inanimate (8)

14 Decipher (7)

16 Wind instrument (6)

18 Sounds off at length (6)

19 Artificial waterway (5)

21 Centre (4)

Across

7 Sumptuously rich (6)

8 Strong and healthy (of a person) (6)

9 Plant with fronds (4)

10 Envisioned (8)

11 Not subject to a levy (3-4)

13 Folded back part of a coat (5)

15 Group of birds (5)

16 Rallying speech (3,4)

18 Minute organisms in the sea (8)

19 Rodents (4)

21 Having sinned (6)

22 Scorched (6)

Down

1 Mammal similar to a large rabbit (4)

2 Remarkably (13)

3 Helicopter (7)

4 Verify (5)

5 Making (13)

6 Extremely delicate (8)

12 Signal that danger is over (3-5)

14 Dampness (7)

17 Trick or feat of daring (5)

20 Bound (4)

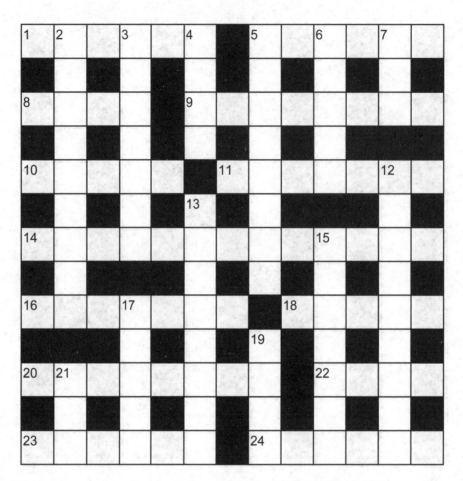

Across

1 Acquired skills (6)
5 Exemplify (6)
8 Link a town with another (4)
9 Obvious (8)
10 Ghost (5)
11 Country in North Africa (7)
14 Perfect likeness or double (8,5)
16 Official proving of a will (7)
18 Cause (havoc) (5)
20 Exaggerated emotion (8)
22 Makes brown (4)
23 External forms (6)
24 Deceive (6)

Down

2 A periodical that is usually daily (9)
3 Make by mixing ingredients (7)
4 Stone block (4)
5 Branch of geometry (8)
6 Money container (5)
7 Cooling tool (3)
12 Firmly established (9)
13 Tanks for storing water (8)
15 Pertaining to matrimony (7)
17 Grips with the teeth (5)
19 Stiff paper (4)
21 Thee (3)

Across

1 Magnifying instruments (11)
9 Hold on to tightly (5)
10 Farewell remark (3)
11 Fairy (5)
12 Tall structure on a castle (5)
13 Wild prank (8)
16 Renounce or reject (8)
18 Network points where lines intersect (5)
21 Stage performer (5)
22 Small sprite (3)
23 Damp (5)
24 Energetically (11)

Down

2 Imprecise (7)
3 Acknowledgement of payment (7)
4 Cut up (6)
5 Should (5)
6 Arm joint (5)
7 Stood for (11)
8 Triangular pyramid (11)
14 Series of boat races (7)
15 Pertaining to warfare (7)
17 Swimming costume (6)
19 Silly (5)
20 Brazilian dance (5)

CROSSWORD 203

Across

1 Throw in the towel (4,2)
7 Lifts up (8)
8 Male child (3)
9 Dodged underneath (6)
10 Matured (4)
11 Conditions (5)
13 Ill-fated (7)
15 Shut in (7)
17 Heating apparatus (5)
21 Char (4)
22 Functional (6)
23 Auction item (3)
24 Corridors (8)
25 Solicited business (6)

Down

1 Device used to seal joints (6)
2 Seller (6)
3 Summits (5)
4 Sheets and blankets (7)
5 Slingshot (8)
6 Decorate (6)
12 Lack of intensity (8)
14 Make less intense (7)
16 Type of confectionery (6)
18 Wildcat (6)
19 Overjoyed (6)
20 Middle of the body (5)

Across

1 Surprise results (6)
4 Nonsense (6)
9 Bodies of writing (7)
10 Stamped (7)
11 Steps on a ladder (5)
12 Mounds of loose sand (5)
14 Plant storage organs (5)
15 Virile (5)
17 Jewel from an oyster shell (5)
18 Edible fish (7)
20 Reaches a specified level (7)
21 Least polite (6)
22 Customary practices (6)

Down

1 Open a wine bottle (6)
2 Diminished in size (8)
3 Runs at a moderate pace (5)
5 E.g. Borneo and Java (7)
6 Anti-aircraft fire (4)
7 Avoids (6)
8 Spanish tennis star (6,5)
13 Working against (8)
14 Past events (7)
15 Garner; collect (6)
16 Narrow-necked bottles (6)
17 Golf shots (5)
19 Eager; keen (4)

CROSSWORD 205

Across

1 Particles around a comet (4)
3 Capital of Australia (8)
9 Lie (7)
10 Sprites (5)
11 Easily (12)
14 Additionally (3)
16 Strong desires (5)
17 Self-esteem (3)
18 Decide in advance (12)
21 Edible pungent bulb (5)
22 Sideways; squinting (7)
23 Took a firm stand (8)
24 Short tail (4)

Down

1 Raised road (8)
2 Dominant theme (5)
4 Fire residue (3)
5 Swimming technique (12)
6 Rotate (7)
7 Too; in addition (4)
8 Environment (12)
12 Not heavy (5)
13 Logical; consistent (8)
15 Redials (anag.) (7)
19 Type of chemical bond (5)
20 Mischievous god in Norse mythology (4)
22 Wonder (3)

Across

1 Caused to stop temporarily (11)

9 One who avoids animal products (5)

10 Bath vessel (3)

11 High lending practice (5)

12 Mark of insertion (5)

13 Coaching (8)

16 Relating to sound (8)

18 Public meeting for open discussion (5)

21 Principle laid down by an authority (5)

22 Charged particle (3)

23 Saying; slogan (5)

24 Brevity in expressing oneself (11)

Down

2 Not artificial (7)

3 Desiring what someone else has (7)

4 District (6)

5 Sudden fear (5)

6 Trees (anag.); organic compound (5)

7 Forged (11)

8 Painting genre (8,3)

14 E.g. use a towel after showering (3-4)

15 Symbols of disgrace (7)

17 Succulent plant (6)

19 Music with a recurrent theme (5)

20 Impersonator (5)

Across

1 Hasty or reckless (4)
3 Sufficiency (8)
9 Spouse (7)
10 Pick out; choose (5)
11 Reduction in value (12)
13 Chest (6)
15 Hold fast (6)
17 Using letters and numbers (12)
20 Wound the pride of (5)
21 Tympanic membrane (7)
22 Component parts (8)
23 Pleased (4)

Down

1 Swiftness (8)
2 Sticky sweet liquid (5)
4 True skin (6)
5 The ? symbol (8,4)
6 Absolutely incredible (7)
7 Legendary creature (4)
8 Perform below expectation (12)
12 Greeted warmly (8)
14 Slanting (7)
16 Place inside something else (6)
18 Rustic (5)
19 Fencing sword (4)

Across

7 Stir dust (anag.) (8)
8 Exclamation on making a mistake (4)
9 Unit of type-size (4)
10 Item used to remember the page you're on (8)
11 Labelling (7)
12 Force upon (5)
15 These grow on your head (5)
17 Ruined; crushed (7)
20 Grandiosity of language (8)
22 Midday (4)
23 Semi-precious agate (4)
24 Using indirect references (8)

Down

1 Sandstone constituent (6)
2 Unknown person (8)
3 Married man (7)
4 Got to one's feet (5)
5 Wander (4)
6 Competitive games (6)
13 Church musician (8)
14 Packages (7)
16 Capital of Greece (6)
18 Change gradually (6)
19 Wide (5)
21 Main body of a book (4)

Across

1 Lookouts (6)
5 Droop (3)
7 Body of rules (5)
8 Chaser (7)
9 Flat-bottomed boat (5)
10 Without shoes (8)
12 Mythical male sea creatures (6)
14 Regal (6)
17 Liberties (8)
18 Slender freshwater fish (5)
20 Positioning (7)
21 Steals (5)
22 Home for a pig (3)
23 Slick and shiny (6)

Down

2 Bravery (7)
3 Expensive fungi (8)
4 Rebuff (4)
5 Catching (7)
6 Entrance (7)
7 Criminal (5)
11 Computer security system (8)
12 Softens with age (7)
13 Majestically (7)
15 Cries for (7)
16 Cuts very short (5)
19 Bent wire for hanging things on (4)

Across

1 Extremely thorough (8)
5 Animal enclosure (4)
8 Requirements (5)
9 Foot support for a rider (7)
10 Remains (7)
12 Hot pepper (7)
14 Highest singing voice (7)
16 Widen (7)
18 Chivalrous (7)
19 Piece of bread (5)
20 Locate or place (4)
21 Speaks very quietly (8)

Down

1 Symbol with magic significance (4)
2 Avaricious (6)
3 Replied (9)
4 Uncertain (6)
6 Wear away (6)
7 Strong type of coffee (8)
11 Excesses (9)
12 Vegetables (8)
13 Cup (6)
14 Steal; seize suddenly (6)
15 For a short time (6)
17 Insects that make honey (4)

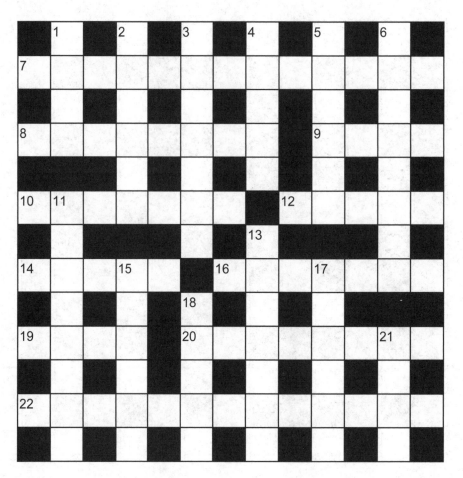

Across

7 Sympathetic and merciful (13)

8 Made level (8)

9 Not strong (4)

10 Quickly (7)

12 Slow down (5)

14 Transparent solid (5)

16 Portions of time (7)

19 Travel on water (4)

20 Appalling (8)

22 Supporting musical part (13)

Down

1 Loud noise (4)

2 Protective kitchen garments (6)

3 Road or roofing material (7)

4 E.g. crows and magpies (5)

5 Reply (6)

6 Took military action against (8)

11 Dependence (8)

13 Listening (7)

15 Jaundiced (6)

17 Phrases that are not taken literally (6)

18 Fellows (5)

21 Lien (anag.) (4)

Across

1 Reduce to a lower grade (6)
4 Grinned (6)
9 Imitate (7)
10 Affairs (7)
11 Ponders (5)
12 Criminal (5)
14 Hard to please (5)
15 Holy chalice (5)
17 Perspire (5)
18 Large island of Indonesia (7)
20 Twirl (7)
21 Meagre (6)
22 Detritus (6)

Down

1 Fanciful; delightful (6)
2 Greek dish (8)
3 Rips (5)
5 Cause to feel very ashamed (7)
6 Part of the ear (4)
7 Small oval plum (6)
8 Show (11)
13 Aromatic shrub (8)
14 Compliment unduly (7)
15 Informal chatter (6)
16 State of mental strain (6)
17 Take hold of (5)
19 Building for grinding grain (4)

Across

1 Every (4)
3 E.g. physics and biology (8)
9 Mapped out in advance (7)
10 Extravagant dinner (5)
11 Corresponding; proportionate (12)
14 Sap (anag.) (3)
16 Electronic device one clicks (5)
17 Research place (abbrev.) (3)
18 Grandeur (12)
21 Clean thoroughly; vegetation (5)
22 Gloomy (7)
23 Fully aware (4-4)
24 Saw; observed (4)

Down

1 Exceptional (8)
2 Deep fissure (5)
4 Partly digested animal food (3)
5 Bubbling (12)
6 Personal possession (7)
7 Hardens (4)
8 Unending (12)
12 Cram (5)
13 Completely preoccupied with (8)
15 Open area of grassland (7)
19 Destitute (5)
20 Capital of Norway (4)
22 Issue legal proceedings (3)

Across

1 Capital of Poland (6)

5 Fasten with stitches (3)

7 Dark beer (5)

8 Unrecoverable sum of money one is owed (3,4)

9 Copper and zinc alloy (5)

10 Contained as part of a whole (8)

12 Fixed periods of work (6)

14 Extravagant meals (6)

17 Grassy clumps (8)

18 Religious book (5)

20 Symbolic objects (7)

21 Attacks without warning (5)

22 Excavated soil (3)

23 Reprimand (6)

Down

2 Contrary to (7)

3 Sufficient (8)

4 Implement for styling hair (4)

5 Drives aground (a boat) (7)

6 Ferocious small mammals (7)

7 Guide a vehicle (5)

11 Capable of being done (8)

12 Turned down (7)

13 Floating mass of frozen water (7)

15 Fusion chamber (7)

16 Melodies (5)

19 Wicked (4)

Across

1 Exertion (6)
5 Chiefly (6)
8 Sharp bristle (4)
9 Upsets; agitates (8)
10 Crown documents (5)
11 Admire deeply (7)
14 Unparalleled (13)
16 Hot water spouts (7)
18 Gaze fixedly (5)
20 Not obligatory (8)
22 Inspires fear (4)
23 Resides (6)
24 Believer in God (6)

Down

2 Perfume (9)
3 Spacecraft that circles the planet (7)
4 Clean up (4)
5 Wrongdoings (8)
6 Base part of a tree (5)
7 High ball in tennis (3)
12 Gloomy (9)
13 Musical wind instruments (8)
15 Nattier (anag.) (7)
17 Motionless (5)
19 Not bumpy; level (4)
21 Animal foot (3)

Across

1 Mend with rows of stitches (4)
3 Automata (8)
9 Prevent from having (7)
10 Singing voices (5)
11 Verification (12)
14 Frozen water (3)
16 Not true (5)
17 One's family (3)
18 Spotless (5-3-4)
21 Main artery (5)
22 Venetian boat (7)
23 Cause frustration (8)
24 Opposite of less (4)

Down

1 Intended to teach (8)
2 Become ready to eat (of fruit) (5)
4 Affirmative vote (3)
5 Very upsetting (5-7)
6 System of interconnected things (7)
7 Cloth worn around the waist (4)
8 Germicide (12)
12 Mediterranean island (5)
13 Deluge (8)
15 Type of sovereign (7)
19 Camera image (abbrev.) (5)
20 Country in West Africa (4)
22 Stomach (3)

CROSSWORD 217

Across

7 Very attractive (of personality) (8)

8 Tells an untruth (4)

9 Devastation (4)

10 Settling for rest (of birds) (8)

11 Technical knowledge (4-3)

12 Round soup containers (5)

15 Phantasm (5)

17 Absence of sound (7)

20 Correctly (8)

22 Set of playing cards (4)

23 A brief piece of film (4)

24 Tangible (8)

Down

1 Sixth planet from the sun (6)

2 Things we are not familiar with (8)

3 Fame (7)

4 Go swiftly (5)

5 Small ink stain (4)

6 Plant of the parsley family (6)

13 Create an account deficit (8)

14 Two-wheeled vehicle (7)

16 Messenger (6)

18 Laugh in a harsh way (6)

19 Clutches tightly (5)

21 Insect stage (4)

Across

1 Peas (anag.) (4)
3 Flammable liquid (8)
9 Floating wreckage (7)
10 Holding or grasping device (5)
11 Enhancements (12)
13 Substance found in wine (6)
15 Plaster for coating walls (6)
17 Practice of designing buildings (12)
20 Avoid (5)
21 Toxin in the body (7)
22 Apparition (8)
23 In a tense state (4)

Down

1 Causes pain or suffering (8)
2 Spy (5)
4 Military forces (6)
5 Quality of being genuine (12)
6 Extreme enthusiast (7)
7 Facial feature (4)
8 Amazement (12)
12 Seriously (8)
14 Perfect happiness (7)
16 Narrow drinking tubes (6)
18 Advised; encouraged (5)
19 Less than average tide (4)

CROSSWORD 219

Across

1 Pulchritude (6)
4 Worldwide (6)
9 Firmly establish (7)
10 Civilian (7)
11 Raised areas of land (5)
12 Opposite of north (5)
14 Timepiece (5)
15 Chart (5)
17 Avarice (5)
18 Tall stand used by a preacher (7)
20 Burdensome work (7)
21 Destitution (6)
22 Warmed up (6)

Down

1 Radiating light (6)
2 Aromatic plant used in cooking (8)
3 Sets of players (5)
5 Boorish (7)
6 Low humming sound (4)
7 Propel with force (6)
8 Doubt (11)
13 Play with great restraint (8)
14 Anybody (7)
15 Ride a horse at pace (6)
16 Mixed up or confused (6)
17 Very serious (5)
19 Piece of metal used as money (4)

Across

7 Masterfully (13)
8 Cosmos (8)
9 Repents (4)
10 Entangle (7)
12 Coin entry points in machines (5)
14 Acknowledged; assumed (5)
16 Primates (7)
19 Thin narrow piece of wood (4)
20 Relight a fire (8)
22 Originality (13)

Down

1 Farm building (4)
2 Precious metal (6)
3 Faintly illuminated at night (7)
4 Snoops (5)
5 Cylindrical wooden container (6)
6 Eloquently (8)
11 Core mass of a country (8)
13 Person who keeps watch (7)
15 Impose or require (6)
17 Pleasant and agreeable (6)
18 Become very hot (5)
21 Oodles (4)

CROSSWORD 221

Across

1 Moving forward at a very slow rate (8)
5 Arrived (4)
8 Electrician (5)
9 Retails (anag.) (7)
10 Tenth month (7)
12 Garden bird (7)
14 Type of alcohol (7)
16 Someone who provides food (7)
18 Cocktail that contains vermouth (7)
19 Care for; look after (5)
20 Plant stem part from which a leaf emerges (4)
21 Clock timing device (8)

Down

1 Domestic cattle (4)
2 Archimedes' famous cry (6)
3 Actor (9)
4 Limited in scope (6)
6 With hands on the hips (6)
7 Outer (8)
11 Opposite of relaxed (9)
12 Sample for medical testing (8)
13 Kept hold of (6)
14 Fur of a stoat (6)
15 Pertaining to a nerve (6)
17 Appear to be (4)

Across

1 Waterproof overshoe (6)
5 Piece of cloth (3)
7 Have in common (5)
8 Pompous language (7)
9 Walked up and down (5)
10 Unsporting activity (4,4)
12 Customer (6)
14 Place of origination (6)
17 Intentionally hidden (8)
18 Cash registers (5)
20 Following immediately (7)
21 Intimidated and weakened (5)
22 Healthy (3)
23 Move in haste (6)

Down

2 Newtlike salamander (7)
3 Franking (8)
4 Type of light (4)
5 Nuclear ___ : device that generates energy (7)
6 Farewell remark (7)
7 Thick slice of beef (5)
11 Relating to courts of law (8)
12 Get rid of (4,3)
13 Vary the pitch of the voice (7)
15 Singer (7)
16 Let air escape from a valve (5)
19 Proverbs (4)

Across

1 Line of police (6)
5 Easily remembered (6)
8 Bite at persistently (4)
9 Small American squirrel (8)
10 Tiny crustaceans (5)
11 At the ocean floor (7)
14 Musical dance co-ordinator (13)
16 Distinct sort or kind (7)
18 Written agreements (5)
20 Rural (8)
22 Comply (4)
23 Posts driven into the ground (6)
24 Not dense (6)

Down

2 State of possessing a thing (9)
3 Someone who dithers (7)
4 Slight cut (4)
5 Mountaineers (8)
6 Measures duration (5)
7 Female chicken (3)
12 Attentiveness (9)
13 Art of controversial discussion (8)
15 Mechanical keyboard (7)
17 Fissure (5)
19 Antelopes (4)
21 Acquire; obtain (3)

Across

1 Deep fissures (6)
4 Disdains (6)
9 Ban on publication (7)
10 The first Gospel (7)
11 Determine the quality of an ore (5)
12 Loose outer garments (5)
14 Feign (3,2)
15 Tarnished (of a metal object) (5)
17 Rejuvenate (5)
18 Insert in a person's body (7)
20 Fortunately (7)
21 Country in central Africa (6)
22 Curved (6)

Down

1 Title of Roman emperors (6)
2 Makes a surprise attack on (8)
3 Compassion (5)
5 Storage tank (7)
6 Wealthy (4)
7 Snarls (6)
8 Proficiently (11)
13 Wave or flourish in display (8)
14 Monumental Egyptian structure (7)
15 Plunderer (6)
16 Moved back and forth (6)
17 Carer (anag.) (5)
19 Large US feline (4)

CROSSWORD 225

Across

7 Amiably (4-9)
8 Tubes for ejecting liquids (8)
9 Jumps on one foot (4)
10 Legal practitioners (7)
12 Journeys (5)
14 Records on tape (5)
16 Disagreement (7)
19 Tolled (4)
20 Proof of something (8)
22 Reflective thought (13)

Down

1 Sacred (4)
2 Nervously (6)
3 Perils (7)
4 Person invited to one's house (5)
5 Current of air (6)
6 Insect trap (8)
11 Troublemaker (8)
13 Perceptible to the eye (7)
15 Strong (6)
17 Make (6)
18 Lines where fabric edges join (5)
21 Lump of earth (4)

Across

1 Female sheep (pl.) (4)
3 People who provide massages (8)
9 Power; strength (7)
10 Supports (5)
11 Uncurled (12)
14 Born (3)
16 Escapade (5)
17 Long and narrow inlet (3)
18 Fortunate; opportune (12)
21 Change (5)
22 Hair-cleansing product (7)
23 Loss of importance or status (8)
24 Basic unit of matter (4)

Down

1 Revealing a truth (8)
2 Consumer (5)
4 Nay (anag.) (3)
5 Underground (12)
6 Uncertain (7)
7 Neither good nor bad (2-2)
8 Not found (12)
12 Wished (5)
13 Dancing hall (8)
15 Error in printing or writing (7)
19 Data entered into a system (5)
20 Mineral powder (4)
22 Lay seed in the ground (3)

CROSSWORD 227

Across

1 Models for a photograph (5)
4 E.g. male and female (7)
7 Closes securely (5)
8 Provoking (8)
9 Becomes worn at the edges (5)
11 Famous Scottish lake (4,4)
15 Sailing vessel (8)
17 Large indefinite amount (5)
19 Maritime (8)
20 Move on ice (5)
21 Prophets (7)
22 Type of sweet (5)

Down

1 Meaningless (9)
2 Make a sucking sound (7)
3 Brother or sister (7)
4 Very tall mythical beings (6)
5 Boring; dull (6)
6 Exchange of tennis strokes (5)
10 Where water meets land (9)
12 The Pope (7)
13 Played out (7)
14 Not moving (6)
16 Moves like a baby (6)
18 Card game (5)

Across

1 Run quickly (4)
3 Cause resentment (8)
9 Diacritical marks (7)
10 Snake toxin (5)
11 Was in first place (3)
12 Crouch (5)
13 Taut (5)
15 Hurt by an insect like a wasp (5)
17 Amends (5)
18 Round bread roll (3)
19 Understood with certainty (5)
20 Male chicken (7)
21 Spread out (8)
22 Remove the skin from (4)

Down

1 Verified again (6-7)
2 Dish of mixed vegetables (5)
4 Pondering (6)
5 Detective (12)
6 Particular languages (7)
7 Device for changing TV channel (6,7)
8 Most perfect example of a quality (12)
14 Foreboding (7)
16 Takes the place of (6)
18 Wash one's body in water (5)

CROSSWORD 229

Across

1 Songbird with a spotted breast (6)
5 Give a nickname to (3)
7 Wonderful (5)
8 Shining (7)
9 Denounce (5)
10 Frequent customers (8)
12 Guarantee (6)
14 Diacritical mark of two dots (6)
17 Philanthropist (8)
18 Hinged barriers between rooms (5)
20 Look into (7)
21 Sharply inclined (5)
22 Domestic animal (3)
23 Eats herbage (6)

Down

2 Listeners (7)
3 Stationery devices (8)
4 Moved quickly (4)
5 Former Greek monetary unit (7)
6 Look after an infant (7)
7 These shine at night (5)
11 Not appropriate (8)
12 Deliver by parachute (3-4)
13 Unaccompanied musician (7)
15 Sudden increase (7)
16 Short high-pitched tone (5)
19 Grain (4)

Across

1 Protest march (abbrev.) (4)
3 Totally clean (8)
9 Stir up trouble (7)
10 Fourth month (5)
11 Slippery fish (3)
12 Acoustic detection system (5)
13 Deprive of weapons (5)
15 Seven (anag.) (5)
17 Unit of heat (5)
18 Trough (3)
19 Pertaining to birds (5)
20 Pear-shaped fruit native to Mexico (7)
21 Overabundances (8)
22 Mischievous sprites (4)

Down

1 Distinguish between (13)
2 Wall painting (5)
4 Surface film; coating (6)
5 Act of sending a message (12)
6 Short trips to perform tasks (7)
7 Sanctimonious (4-9)
8 Calculations of dimensions (12)
14 Mournful (7)
16 Large property with land (6)
18 Kingdom (5)

CROSSWORD 231

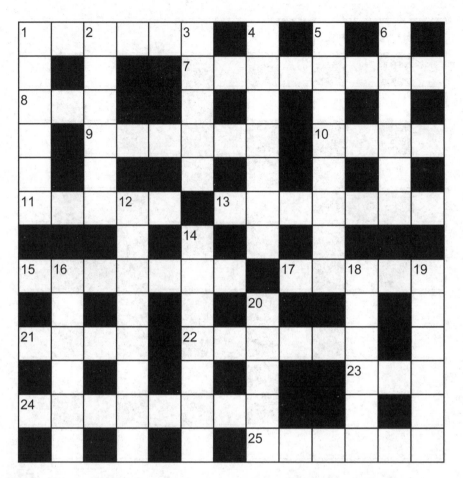

Across

1 Fairly (6)
7 Distinction; high status (8)
8 Great distress (3)
9 Kept private; unknown by others (6)
10 Metal thread (4)
11 Makeshift shelter (5)
13 Aquatic reptiles (7)
15 Small onion-like bulb (7)
17 Falls to the ground (5)
21 Seize (4)
22 Migratory grasshopper (6)
23 Assist (3)
24 Relating to deep feelings (8)
25 Spring suddenly (6)

Down

1 Precious stones (6)
2 Afternoon sleep (6)
3 Resay (anag.) (5)
4 Rowdy (7)
5 Contents of the Mediterranean (8)
6 Rarely encountered (6)
12 Summon to return (4,4)
14 Sad and abandoned (7)
16 Abominable (6)
18 Get hold of (6)
19 Thick wet mud (6)
20 Skin on top of the head (5)

Across

1 Foolish (4)
3 Large metal pot (8)
9 Pertaining to the heart (7)
10 Combines (5)
11 Precondition (12)
13 A way out (6)
15 Situated within a building (6)
17 Not special (3-2-3-4)
20 Monster with nine heads (5)
21 Wanting (7)
22 Evacuating (8)
23 Ancient harp (4)

Down

1 Interpret the meaning of (8)
2 Compel (5)
4 Increase over time (6)
5 Jail term without end (4,8)
6 Italian dish (7)
7 Where a bird lays eggs (4)
8 Designed to distract (12)
12 Preliminary speech (8)
14 Summary of events (5-2)
16 Taken illegally (6)
18 Coldly (5)
19 Type of footwear (4)

CROSSWORD 233

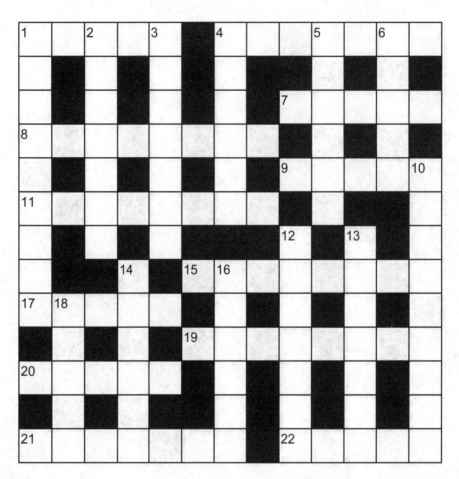

Across

1 Mopes (5)
4 Hobby (7)
7 Non-flowering plants (5)
8 Form of make-up (8)
9 Overly self-assertive (5)
11 Mountainous region (8)
15 Annul or abolish (8)
17 Talked audibly (5)
19 Ornamental jet of water (8)
20 Gets larger (5)
21 Patio or veranda (7)
22 Post (5)

Down

1 Minor exhibitions (9)
2 Ancestry (7)
3 Airless (anag.) (7)
4 Common bird (6)
5 Belonging to them (6)
6 Looks after temporarily (5)
10 Sleep through winter (9)
12 Points where edges meet (7)
13 Island in the West Indies (7)
14 Long pin (6)
16 Woman's garment (6)
18 Clean spiritually (5)

Across

1 Assurance; composure (6)
7 Fetch (8)
8 Nourished (3)
9 South American cowboy (6)
10 Engage in spirited fun (4)
11 Challenges (5)
13 Showy flowers (7)
15 Fragment (7)
17 Tennis score (5)
21 Japanese sport (4)
22 Pictures (6)
23 First woman (3)
24 Impetus (8)
25 Noises (6)

Down

1 Have sufficient money to pay for (6)
2 Person staying in another's home (6)
3 Clay block (5)
4 Caresses (7)
5 Aggressive use of force (8)
6 Strongly opposed (6)
12 Researched in detail (8)
14 Renaissance (7)
16 Nerve cell (6)
18 Not noticed (6)
19 Leases (anag.) (6)
20 Pacifies (5)

CROSSWORD 235

Across

1 Garden implement (4)
3 Portable device to keep rain out (8)
9 In the middle (7)
10 Sacred hymn or song (5)
11 Type of contest (12)
13 Lengthen (6)
15 Style of popular music (6)
17 Despair (12)
20 First Greek letter (5)
21 Process of wearing away (7)
22 Totally in love with (8)
23 Cure of disease; mend (4)

Down

1 Rebound (8)
2 Country in East Africa (5)
4 Free from discord (6)
5 Act of reclamation (12)
6 Inclination (7)
7 Ends; goals (4)
8 Surpassing in influence (12)
12 Individual; private (8)
14 Groups of actors (7)
16 Remove; excise (6)
18 Join together; merge (5)
19 Spread clumsily on a surface (4)

Across

7 Thin layer of sedimentary rock (6)
8 Ringer (anag.) (6)
9 Mass of floating ice (4)
10 Food portions (8)
11 Museum keeper (7)
13 Projecting horizontal ledge (5)
15 Cooks in the oven (5)
16 Hermit (7)
18 Soak; drench (8)
19 Precious metal (4)
21 Tentacle (6)
22 Goes to see someone (6)

Down

1 Cabbagelike plant (4)
2 Shamefully (13)
3 Emotion (7)
4 Polar ___ : large mammals (5)
5 Zoologist who studies birds (13)
6 Cuddles up (8)
12 Unexpectedly (8)
14 Mislead on purpose (7)
17 Store that sells milk products (5)
20 Stringed instrument (4)

CROSSWORD 237

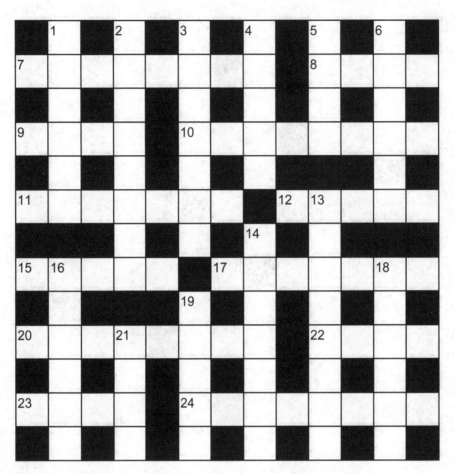

Across

7 Repress (8)
8 Underwater ridge of rock (4)
9 Blessing (4)
10 Industrious (8)
11 Responses (7)
12 Clock pointers (5)
15 Skilled job (5)
17 Periodical (7)
20 Putting into practice (8)
22 Empty space (4)
23 Short pins that taper at one end (4)
24 Ruler (8)

Down

1 Extract meaning from (6)
2 Deadlock (5-3)
3 Outlaws (7)
4 Small hill (5)
5 Medicine (4)
6 Controlled; restrained (6)
13 Opposite of departures (8)
14 Non-pedigree dog (7)
16 Torn (of clothes) (6)
18 Bird enclosure (6)
19 Clod of turf (5)
21 Girl or young woman (4)

Across

1 Cipher (4)
3 E.g. sketches (8)
9 United States (7)
10 Excess (5)
11 Item of value (5)
12 Oval shape (7)
13 Recurrent topics (6)
15 Oar (6)
17 Bring a law into effect again (2-5)
18 Precipitates (5)
20 Number after seven (5)
21 Not in any place (7)
22 Made unhappy (8)
23 Exploits (4)

Down

1 Dull and uninteresting (13)
2 Songs for two people (5)
4 Machine that harvests a crop (6)
5 Small garden carts (12)
6 Collection of sheets of paper (7)
7 Brazenness (13)
8 Chatter (6-6)
14 Came into view (7)
16 Attitude or body position (6)
19 Mental impressions (5)

CROSSWORD 239

Across

1 Falls out unintentionally (6)
5 Stimulate (6)
8 Acquire (4)
9 Changing (8)
10 Rebuffs (5)
11 Jumpy (7)
14 Fitness to fly (13)
16 Period of relief (7)
18 Wanes (anag.) (5)
20 Showing embarrassment (8)
22 Knowledge (abbrev.) (4)
23 Homes (6)
24 Small worry; irritate (6)

Down

2 Sounding mournful (9)
3 Archer's weapon (7)
4 Sewing join (4)
5 Vision (8)
6 Military trainee (5)
7 Unit of weight (3)
12 Indignant (9)
13 Nitrogenous organic compounds (8)
15 Requiring (7)
17 Ask for earnestly (5)
19 At what time (4)
21 Cooking appliance (3)

Across

7 Tremendously (13)
8 Event (8)
9 Hogs (4)
10 One who holds property for another (7)
12 Opposite of sink (5)
14 Sound a duck makes (5)
16 Freedom (7)
19 Photographic material (4)
20 Soonest (8)
22 Forever honest (13)

Down

1 Young deer (4)
2 Removes all coverings from (6)
3 Showed a person to their seat (7)
4 Clenched hands (5)
5 Part of a flower (6)
6 Obviously offensive (of an action) (8)
11 Social gatherings for old friends (8)
13 Play havoc with (7)
15 Widespread (6)
17 Evoke (6)
18 Reads (anag.) (5)
21 River sediment (4)

CROSSWORD 241

Across

1 Despise (4)

3 Distinguishing mark (8)

9 Cutting back a tree (7)

10 Domesticates (5)

11 Tear (3)

12 Passenger ship (5)

13 Suppress (5)

15 Chopping (5)

17 Teacher (5)

18 Consumed food (3)

19 Small boat (5)

20 Slope (7)

21 Secret relationships (8)

22 Marries (4)

Down

1 Excessively negative about (13)

2 Outdo (5)

4 Invalidate (6)

5 Ability to acquire and apply knowledge (12)

6 Existing solely in name (7)

7 Aggressive self-assurance (13)

8 Squint harder (anag.) (12)

14 Round building (7)

16 E.g. from New Delhi (6)

18 Nimble (5)

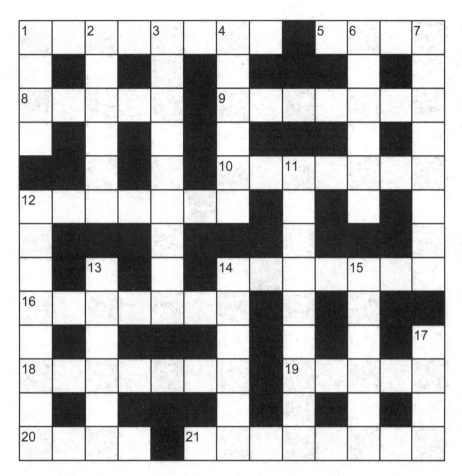

Across

1 Substantial; not elusive (8)
5 Small drink of whisky (4)
8 Business proposal; playing field (5)
9 Necessity (7)
10 Slowly moving mass of ice (7)
12 Visible horizon (7)
14 Financiers (7)
16 Stronghold (7)
18 Irregularity (7)
19 Abrupt (5)
20 Observed (4)
21 Spider (8)

Down

1 Recording medium (4)
2 Inform (6)
3 Received by genetic transmission (9)
4 Living room (6)
6 Smelling horrible (of old food) (6)
7 Female head of a town (8)
11 Concerned with beauty (9)
12 Slipcase (anag.) (8)
13 Flashing light (6)
14 Participant in a game (6)
15 Move faster than (6)
17 Clutched (4)

CROSSWORD 243

Across

7 Break (8)
8 Breathing organ (4)
9 Slightly curling lock of hair (4)
10 Alert in advance (8)
11 Put money in the bank (7)
12 Untidy (5)
15 Joint (5)
17 Opposite of failure (7)
20 A magical quality (8)
22 Dell (4)
23 Seabird (4)
24 Social isolation (8)

Down

1 Wrinkle (6)
2 Ranks in society (8)
3 Excess (7)
4 Perceives audibly (5)
5 Exhaled hard (4)
6 Growls (6)
13 Dig out (8)
14 Easily drawn out into a wire (7)
16 More precisely (6)
18 Dishes of leafy greens (6)
19 Arduous search for something (5)
21 Ladder step (4)

Across

1 Indistinct (6)
4 Worshipped (6)
9 Bathing tub with bubbles (7)
10 Climbing tools (7)
11 Fat-like compound (5)
12 Coral reef (5)
14 Element with atomic number 5 (5)
15 Shapely (5)
17 Surface upon which one walks (5)
18 Cultured; elegant (7)
20 Eagerness (7)
21 Church buildings (6)
22 Put on a play (6)

Down

1 Coax into doing something (6)
2 Dweller (8)
3 Bewildered (5)
5 Impassive (7)
6 Frost (4)
7 Maiden (6)
8 Award for coming second (6,5)
13 Approaching (8)
14 Eventually (2,3,2)
15 Gaseous envelope of the sun (6)
16 Made a victim of (6)
17 Only just able to be seen (5)
19 Body fat (4)

CROSSWORD 245

Across

1 Containers (4)
3 Viewing (8)
9 Least difficult (7)
10 Scheme intended to deceive (3-2)
11 Place of conflict (12)
14 Flightless bird (3)
16 Enthusiasm (5)
17 Pair of actors (3)
18 Brutally; harshly (12)
21 Birds do this to clean their feathers (5)
22 Father of a parent (7)
23 Rays of natural light (8)
24 Curved shape (4)

Down

1 Quivered (8)
2 Attack on all sides (5)
4 What painters create (3)
5 Worldly (12)
6 Chanted (7)
7 Stare with an open mouth (4)
8 Hostile aggressiveness (12)
12 E.g. oxygen and nitrogen (5)
13 Person of varied learning (8)
15 Indefinitely many (7)
19 Sea duck (5)
20 Musical composition (4)
22 Sticky substance (3)

Across

1 Pleasant scents (8)
5 Tibetan Buddhist monk (4)
9 Glisten (5)
10 Ceases (5)
11 How something looks (10)
14 Make better (6)
15 Join together (6)
17 Following in a logical order (10)
20 Iron alloy (5)
21 Opposite of thin (5)
22 Takes an exam (4)
23 Underprivileged (8)

Down

1 Luxurious (4)
2 Liquid precipitation (4)
3 By chance (12)
4 Discharges (6)
6 Legendary island (8)
7 Responded to (8)
8 Carport choir (anag.) (12)
12 Continues obstinately (8)
13 Regular (8)
16 Firmly fixed (6)
18 Capital of the Ukraine (4)
19 Slide; lose grip (4)

CROSSWORD 247

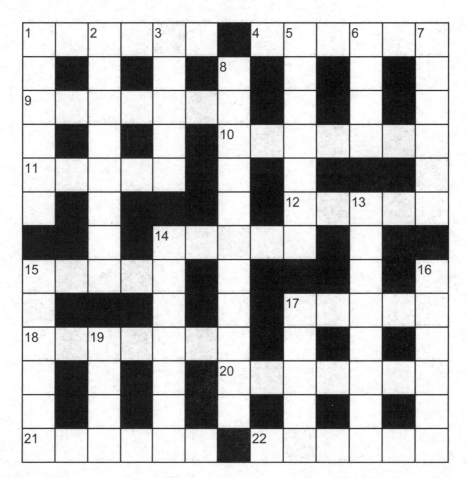

Across

- **1** Go around (6)
- **4** Lethargy (6)
- **9** Keepsake; reminder (7)
- **10** Govern badly (7)
- **11** Vegetables (5)
- **12** Commerce (5)
- **14** Indoor game (5)
- **15** Form of identification (5)
- **17** Artifice (5)
- **18** Rich sweet roll (7)
- **20** Pertaining to marriage (7)
- **21** Demands; insists on (6)
- **22** Sayings (6)

Down

- **1** Speak in a confused way (6)
- **2** Overindulged (8)
- **3** Basins (5)
- **5** Compensates for (7)
- **6** Country in South America (4)
- **7** Withdraw (6)
- **8** Dignified manner or conduct (11)
- **13** Praising (anag.) (8)
- **14** Discourse on a theme (7)
- **15** Talk foolishly (6)
- **16** Abilities; talents (6)
- **17** Used a computer keyboard (5)
- **19** Small quantity (4)

Across

1 Superior of a nunnery (6)
7 Exaggerated (8)
8 Vessel; jolt (3)
9 Thin strip of wood (6)
10 Opposite of shut (4)
11 Gets weary (5)
13 Trying experiences (7)
15 Fabric (7)
17 Warhorse (5)
21 Freezes over (4)
22 Apparatus for heating water (6)
23 Seabird (3)
24 E.g. from Italy or Spain (8)
25 Medical practitioner (6)

Down

1 Alter or adapt (6)
2 One who manages finances at a college (6)
3 Of definite shape (5)
4 Occidental (7)
5 Language used by an individual (8)
6 Uncover (6)
12 Outpouring (8)
14 Short close-fitting jacket (7)
16 Involuntary spasm (6)
18 Straying from the right course (6)
19 Not as light (6)
20 Evil spirit (5)

CROSSWORD 249

Across

1 Become dim (4)
3 Pertaining to education (8)
9 Clinging shellfish (7)
10 Silk fabric (5)
11 Unit of weight (5)
12 Approve or support (7)
13 Pollutes (6)
15 Outlaw (6)
17 Violent troublemakers (7)
18 Ballroom dance (5)
20 Join together (5)
21 Cleanliness (7)
22 International waters (4,4)
23 Wet with condensation (4)

Down

1 Continue a stroke in tennis (6,7)
2 Evil spirit (5)
4 Small box (6)
5 Drawback (12)
6 Developed (7)
7 Sweets (13)
8 Notwithstanding (12)
14 Smoothing clothes (7)
16 Respiratory condition (6)
19 Female relation (5)

Across

1 Falls behind (4)
3 Knitted jacket (8)
9 Hide (7)
10 Stanza of a poem (5)
11 Omit too much detail (12)
13 Holy (6)
15 Abdominal organ (6)
17 Effects or results (12)
20 Large marine mammal (5)
21 Changed (7)
22 Best (8)
23 Go by an indirect route (4)

Down

1 Field game (8)
2 Spirit in a bottle (5)
4 Ablaze (6)
5 Changes to a situation (12)
6 Tall quadruped (7)
7 Christmas (4)
8 Re-evaluation (12)
12 Unequal (3-5)
14 Stately hymn tune (7)
16 Crouches down (6)
18 Cut a joint of meat (5)
19 Loot (4)

CROSSWORD 251

Across

1 Narrow trench (6)
5 Turn into (6)
8 Animal doctors (4)
9 Fixtures (8)
10 Group of notes played simultaneously (5)
11 Soothsayer (7)
14 Ease of use or entry (13)
16 Nervous excitement (7)
18 Examines quickly (5)
20 Motionless (8)
22 Journey (4)
23 Those expelled from a country (6)
24 Growing dimmer (6)

Down

2 Amoral (9)
3 Rise again (7)
4 Drift in the air (4)
5 Garment worn after a shower (8)
6 Sing like a bird (5)
7 Cup (3)
12 Addition to a building (9)
13 Austere people (8)
15 Found (7)
17 Unpleasant facial expression (5)
19 A person's individuality (4)
21 Blend together (3)

CROSSWORD 252

Across

1 Thespians (6)
5 Roll of bank notes (3)
7 Enamel-coated structure (5)
8 Extend an arm or leg (7)
9 Thigh bone (5)
10 Bedrooms (8)
12 Fix (6)
14 Ghost (6)
17 Porcelain (8)
18 Smells strongly (5)
20 Removing frost from a windscreen (2-5)
21 Assumed name (5)
22 Opposite of cold (3)
23 Gazes at (6)

Down

2 Negative electrode (7)
3 Modify with new parts (8)
4 Barking sound (4)
5 Whine softly (7)
6 Thaw (7)
7 Bronze medal position (5)
11 Beekeeper (8)
12 Renew (7)
13 Weasel-like animal (7)
15 Fragrant compound (7)
16 Fixes (5)
19 List (anag.) (4)

CROSSWORD 253

Across

7 Interrogate (8)

8 Burden (4)

9 Remedy (4)

10 Large Eurasian maple (8)

11 Intoxicating element in wine (7)

12 Fop (5)

15 Dirty (5)

17 Last beyond (7)

20 Distance across a circle (8)

22 Wish for (4)

23 Areas of ground for growing plants (4)

24 Quality of being considerate (8)

Down

1 Reciprocal (6)

2 Space rock (8)

3 Assignment; errand (7)

4 Natural talent (5)

5 Literary composition (4)

6 Rotten (6)

13 Permitting (8)

14 Present (7)

16 Gets together (6)

18 Disappear (6)

19 Tend a fire (5)

21 Facial disguise (4)

CROSSWORD 254

Across

1 Freedom from dirt (11)

9 Prohibited by social custom (5)

10 Sheltered side (3)

11 Construct (5)

12 Will (5)

13 Glass container for displaying objects (8)

16 Collection in its entirety (8)

18 Russian sovereigns (5)

21 Not dead (5)

22 Bite sharply (3)

23 Republic in the Middle East (5)

24 Not wanted (11)

Down

2 Vocabulary list (7)

3 Artistic movement (3,4)

4 Identifying tags (6)

5 Crevices (5)

6 Latin American dance (5)

7 Act of looking after children (11)

8 Substitute (11)

14 European country (7)

15 Commander in chief of a fleet (7)

17 Graduates of a college (6)

19 Trembling poplar (5)

20 Manner of speaking (5)

CROSSWORD 255

Across

1 Comfort in times of misfortune (6)
5 Deity (3)
7 Track of an animal (5)
8 Adorn with precious stones (7)
9 Door hanger (5)
10 Take away (8)
12 Contemptibly small (6)
14 Recapture (6)
17 Coagulating (8)
18 Slabs of peat for fuel (5)
20 Type of treatment for a disorder (7)
21 Disreputable; underhand (5)
22 Floor covering (3)
23 Powerful (6)

Down

2 Exploit to excess (7)
3 Faint-hearted (8)
4 Nocturnal insect (4)
5 A parent's mother (7)
6 Illness (7)
7 Suave (5)
11 Support at the top of a seat (8)
12 Trimmed (anag.) (7)
13 Part of a chair (7)
15 Central bolt (7)
16 Outdated (5)
19 Immerse in liquid (4)

Across

7 Spoof (6)
8 Donors (anag.) (6)
9 Hit with a lash (4)
10 Journey across (8)
11 Powerful dog (7)
13 Wild and untamed (5)
15 Side posts of doorways (5)
16 Decaying (7)
18 Easy chair (8)
19 Make fun of (4)
21 Alphabetical character (6)
22 Pointless (6)

Down

1 Speed relative to sound (4)
2 Ability to get along (13)
3 Bewilder (7)
4 Make inoperative (5)
5 Value too lowly (13)
6 One who steers a boat (8)
12 Woke up (8)
14 Shock greatly (7)
17 ___ Agassi: former tennis star (5)
20 Not hot (4)

CROSSWORD 257

Across

1 State of the USA (4)
3 Loyal and hard-working (8)
9 Readable (7)
10 Type of jazz (5)
11 Enraging worm (anag.) (12)
14 Pot (3)
16 Not in good physical condition (5)
17 Trouble in body or mind (3)
18 Limitless (12)
21 Wash with water (5)
22 Immature and childish (7)
23 Canine (3,5)
24 Stitches (4)

Down

1 Illegal (8)
2 Tool for boring holes (5)
4 Draw (3)
5 Scientific research rooms (12)
6 European country (7)
7 Jar lids (4)
8 Lowest possible temperature (8,4)
12 Presents (5)
13 Totally uninformed (8)
15 Person proposed for office (7)
19 Inducement (5)
20 Soft cheese (4)
22 Touch gently (3)

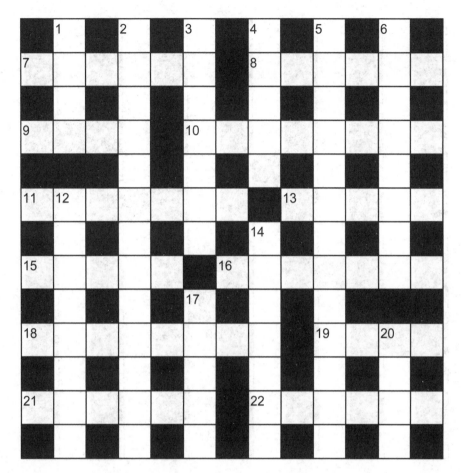

Across

7 Main meal (6)

8 Yearly (6)

9 Pile (4)

10 One totally opposed to violence (8)

11 Position on top of (7)

13 Shafts dug to obtain water (5)

15 Ruin (5)

16 Jumpers (7)

18 Hard shell of a crustacean (8)

19 Disgusting (4)

21 Howl (6)

22 Underground storage area (6)

Down

1 Snide comment (4)

2 Not fully valued (13)

3 Vivid (7)

4 Whim or caprice; find attractive (5)

5 Harmlessly (13)

6 Casually (anag.) (8)

12 Quality of being different (8)

14 Request earnestly (7)

17 Areas of agricultural land (5)

20 Give temporarily (4)

CROSSWORD 259

Across

1 Increase; extend (6)
5 Waste matter (6)
8 Popular martial art (4)
9 Anticlimax (8)
10 Threshing tool (5)
11 Costing (anag.) (7)
14 Remove dangerous substances from (13)
16 Flight attendant (7)
18 Fluffy (5)
20 Everlasting (8)
22 Anger or irritate (4)
23 Velocities (6)
24 Lanes (6)

Down

2 Exuberant (9)
3 Precondition (7)
4 Religious sisters (4)
5 Words with similar meanings (8)
6 Oscillations in water (5)
7 Trap; ensnare (3)
12 Mutual influence or action (9)
13 Utters repeatedly (8)
15 Impartial (7)
17 Complete (5)
19 Prayer (4)
21 Soak up; wipe away (3)

Across

1 Tune (6)
4 Keen insight (6)
9 Violent and lawless person (7)
10 Having great wisdom (7)
11 Hurried (5)
12 Raised to the third power (5)
14 Expect to happen (5)
15 Alcoholic drinks made from grapes (5)
17 Roman country house (5)
18 Move; agitate (7)
20 Game where success is based on luck (7)
21 Broken fragments of glass (6)
22 Prayer (6)

Down

1 Waterlogged (6)
2 Longevity of an individual (8)
3 God (5)
5 Reduce in size (7)
6 Relocate (4)
7 Tensed (anag.) (6)
8 Indescribable (11)
13 People who construct things (8)
14 Taken as true (7)
15 Jams tight (6)
16 Deep gorge (6)
17 Elector (5)
19 Gull-like bird (4)

CROSSWORD 261

Across

1 Escorted (11)
9 Attempts (5)
10 Excellent serve (3)
11 Up to the time when (5)
12 Fight (3-2)
13 Handouts (anag.) (8)
16 Piece for a soloist and orchestra (8)
18 Happen again (5)
21 Narrow roads (5)
22 Meat from a pig (3)
23 Shrewdness; understanding (5)
24 Logical coherence (11)

Down

2 Warning (7)
3 Live longer than (7)
4 Jail (6)
5 Birds lay their eggs in these (5)
6 Make law (5)
7 Reliable (11)
8 Tunefully (11)
14 Assistant (7)
15 Frenzied (7)
17 Small oval fruits (6)
19 Brief appearance in a film by someone famous (5)
20 Takes a break (5)

Across

1 Three times (6)
5 Cuddle (3)
7 Happy; jovial (5)
8 Moderately slow tempo (music) (7)
9 Spiny yellow-flowered shrub (5)
10 Constricts (8)
12 Pressing keys (6)
14 Increases a gap (6)
17 Harshness (8)
18 Spike used by a climber (5)
20 Learn new skills (7)
21 Silly (5)
22 Lyric poem (3)
23 Small spots or dots (6)

Down

2 Conveniently (7)
3 Invariable (8)
4 Long and laborious work (4)
5 Cause to absorb water (7)
6 Not solid or liquid (7)
7 Clothing made from denim (5)
11 Move out the way of (8)
12 Underwater projectile (7)
13 Apprentice (7)
15 Quibble (7)
16 Edible fruit (5)
19 Cranny (4)

Across

1 Device for inflating tyres (4)
3 Predator (anag.) (8)
9 Keep out (7)
10 Group of witches (5)
11 Form of oxygen found in the atmosphere (5)
12 Non-specific (7)
13 Persuasive and logical; clear (6)
15 Bear witness (6)
17 Chatter (7)
18 Musical times (5)
20 Bring on oneself (5)
21 Part of a fortification (7)
22 Holding close (8)
23 Church song (4)

Down

1 Presupposition (13)
2 Extremely small (prefix) (5)
4 Come into view (6)
5 Build up again from parts (12)
6 Daydream (7)
7 Scared (5-8)
8 Occult (12)
14 Sideways looks (7)
16 Complain about (6)
19 Sullen; morose (5)

Across

1 Opposite of highest (6)

5 Finish first (3)

7 Soft type of rock (5)

8 Designer of trendy clothes (7)

9 Daft (5)

10 Many and various (8)

12 Be owned by (6)

14 Pedestrian (6)

17 Printed version of data on a computer (4,4)

18 Looked at open-mouthed (5)

20 Coped (7)

21 Competes in a speed contest (5)

22 Deranged (3)

23 Strangest (6)

Down

2 Go faster than (7)

3 Breathing in sharply (8)

4 Labels (4)

5 Matrimony (7)

6 This starts on 1st January (3,4)

7 Main plant stem (5)

11 Forgave (8)

12 European country (7)

13 Large spotted cat (7)

15 Female ruler (7)

16 Lamps (anag.) (5)

19 Slender freshwater fish (4)

CROSSWORD 265

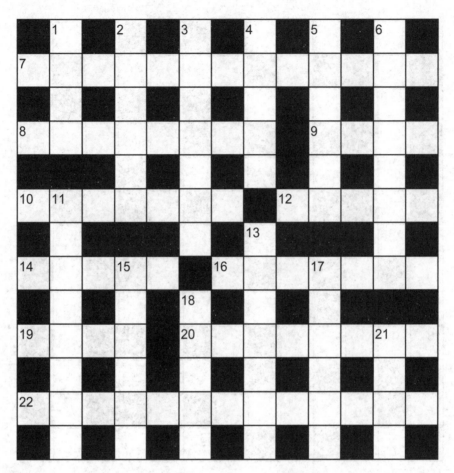

Across

7 Holier-than-thou (13)
8 Shining (8)
9 Liquid food (4)
10 Avoidance (7)
12 Absorbent pads (5)
14 Chute (5)
16 People who manage college finances (7)
19 Heat up (4)
20 Inn (8)
22 Relating to growth (13)

Down

1 Correctional institution (4)
2 Morsels of food (6)
3 Guest (7)
4 Flour and water mixture (5)
5 Puzzle composed of many pieces (6)
6 Long green vegetable (8)
11 Small communities (8)
13 Copious (7)
15 Not as bright (6)
17 Yellowish-brown pigment (6)
18 Vibrated (5)
21 Thoroughfare (4)

Across

1 Enthusiastic supporter (11)
9 Showing a willingness to achieve results (3-2)
10 Animal lair (3)
11 Twilled cotton fabric (5)
12 Less (5)
13 Rigorous appraisal (4,4)
16 Expression of gratitude (5,3)
18 Walk heavily and firmly (5)
21 Section of a long poem (5)
22 Viscous liquid (3)
23 Talk (5)
24 Having celebrities in attendance (4-7)

Down

2 Taxonomic group including humans (7)
3 Bodyguards (7)
4 Wildcats (6)
5 Remote in manner (5)
6 Equip (5)
7 Proclamation (11)
8 Unwilling to believe (11)
14 Bumped into (7)
15 Poison (7)
17 Not disposed to cheat (6)
19 Dole out (5)
20 Show-off (5)

Across

7 Grateful (8)
8 Bovine animals (4)
9 Burrowing mammal (4)
10 Unyielding (8)
11 Trespass (7)
12 Strength (5)
15 Tumble from a horse (5)
17 Small house (7)
20 Pasta in the form of narrow ribbons (8)
22 Seep; exude (4)
23 Hold as an opinion (4)
24 Scatter in drops (8)

Down

1 Easy victory (4-2)
2 Essential or fundamental (8)
3 Has enough money to pay for (7)
4 Move effortlessly through the air (5)
5 Stern and forbidding (4)
6 Group of seven (6)
13 Sociable (8)
14 People who behave affectedly (7)
16 Costs (6)
18 Drink greedily (6)
19 Top degree mark (5)
21 Smug (anag.) (4)

Across

1 Extreme bitterness (8)
5 Gelatinous substance (4)
8 Decompose (5)
9 Ingenuous (7)
10 Petitions to God (7)
12 Competitors in a sprint (7)
14 One more (7)
16 Comes up with a plan (7)
18 Embryonic root (7)
19 Entice to do something (5)
20 Fathers (4)
21 Mileage tracker (8)

Down

1 Helper; assistant (4)
2 Calculate (6)
3 Reveries (9)
4 Travels on foot (6)
6 Diving waterbirds (6)
7 Sorriest (anag.) (8)
11 Botanical garden for trees (9)
12 Provided a service (8)
13 Avoided (6)
14 Climb (6)
15 Recluse (6)
17 Heavenly body (4)

CROSSWORD 269

Across

1 Gaming cubes (4)
3 Settlers (anag.) (8)
9 Substance used to remove heat (7)
10 Sharp blade (5)
11 From this time on (12)
13 Son of one's brother or sister (6)
15 Botch (4-2)
17 Significant (12)
20 ___ syrup: pancake topping (5)
21 Serving no purpose (7)
22 Beat out grain (8)
23 Norse god of thunder (4)

Down

1 Crew member (on a ship) (8)
2 Headgear of a monarch (5)
4 Share out food sparingly (6)
5 Sweet red fruits (12)
6 Four-legged reptiles (7)
7 Forefather (4)
8 Failure to act with prudence (12)
12 Peacemaker (8)
14 Succeed financially (7)
16 Advance evidence for (6)
18 Large tree (5)
19 Small flake of soot (4)

Across

1 Popular round fruits (6)

7 Easy victory (8)

8 Bleat of a sheep (3)

9 Red wine (6)

10 Emit light (4)

11 Seed cases (5)

13 Part of a horse's leg (7)

15 Looked up to (7)

17 Long-legged bird (5)

21 Depression in a surface (4)

22 Natural skill (6)

23 Sort; kind (3)

24 Unselfish concern for others (8)

25 Senior tribal figures (6)

Down

1 Surprise attack (6)

2 Puts in position (6)

3 Declared solemnly (5)

4 Flap the wings quickly (of a bird) (7)

5 Country in Central Asia (8)

6 Very brave and courageous (6)

12 Trinkets (anag.) (8)

14 Free from doubt (7)

16 Profoundly (6)

18 Grammatical case (6)

19 Commotion (6)

20 Body of burning gas (5)

CROSSWORD 271

Across

1 Parody (6)
4 Beat soundly (6)
9 Version of a book (7)
10 Idealist; visionary (7)
11 Irritable (5)
12 Colossus (5)
14 Raises up (5)
15 Scoundrel (5)
17 Lifting device (5)
18 Design of fashionable clothes (7)
20 Provoked or teased (7)
21 Subject to a penalty (6)
22 Spirited (6)

Down

1 Guides (6)
2 Winding strands about each other (8)
3 Showery (5)
5 Takes into custody (7)
6 Apparatus for weaving (4)
7 Financier (6)
8 Unconcerned (11)
13 Sparkles (8)
14 Peas and beans (7)
15 Regain (6)
16 Of inferior quality (6)
17 In what place (5)
19 On top of (4)

Across

1 Opposite of pulled (6)
7 Fills with air (8)
8 Enjoyable (3)
9 US state of islands (6)
10 Make a garment using wool (4)
11 Loves uncritically (5)
13 Encroach (7)
15 Splash (7)
17 Undergarments (5)
21 Molten rock (4)
22 Fairness (6)
23 Boy (3)
24 Cutting wood (8)
25 Displayed freely (6)

Down

1 Breathless (6)
2 Item worn on the head on a hot day (3,3)
3 Female opera singers (5)
4 States as a fact (7)
5 Say mean things about another (8)
6 Annoying (6)
12 Measure of the heat content of a system (8)
14 Advantage gained from something (7)
16 Fine; great (6)
18 Fashioned (6)
19 Protected from sunlight (6)
20 Move out of the way (5)

CROSSWORD 273

Across

1 Dough used for pies (6)
4 Chaos (6)
9 Disturb (7)
10 Plant of the buttercup family (7)
11 Insanely (5)
12 Things to be done (5)
14 Moneys owed (5)
15 Small woodland (5)
17 Smash into another vehicle (5)
18 Item of clerical clothing (7)
20 Brought to bear (7)
21 Argue against (6)
22 Cowers (anag.) (6)

Down

1 State of matter (6)
2 Superficial (4-4)
3 Fully prepared (5)
5 Characteristics; features (7)
6 Brave person; idol (4)
7 Short choral compositions (6)
8 Crushed with sorrow (11)
13 Scatter upon impact (8)
14 Dedicates (7)
15 Bird; crazy (6)
16 Follow closely (6)
17 Strategic board game (5)
19 Retail establishment (4)

Across

7 Merciful (6)
8 Loose part of a garment (6)
9 Welsh emblem (4)
10 Not long ago (8)
11 Slow mover (7)
13 Pile (5)
15 Capital of France (5)
16 Timidity (7)
18 Person who maintains machines (8)
19 Area of mown grass (4)
21 Child (6)
22 Not malignant (6)

Down

1 Third Gospel (4)
2 Lazy (13)
3 Small dog (7)
4 Sudden jerk (5)
5 Nervy or scary (5-8)
6 Substitutes (8)
12 Discovering; finding out (8)
14 Thus; as a result (7)
17 Mooring for a ship (5)
20 Hairpieces (4)

CROSSWORD 275

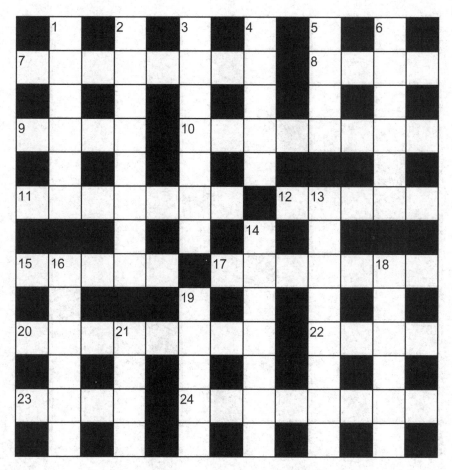

Across

7 Refined and elegant (8)
8 Big cat (4)
9 Dairy product (4)
10 Huge (8)
11 Emit energy (7)
12 Wind instrument (5)
15 Pond-dwelling amphibians (5)
17 Go before (7)
20 Devilry (8)
22 Hollow cylinder (4)
23 Chief god of ancient Greece (4)
24 Madness (8)

Down

1 Emotional shock (6)
2 Sailing swiftly (8)
3 Personal belongings (7)
4 Darkness (5)
5 Dejected (4)
6 Vigorous; strong and healthy (6)
13 Finding (8)
14 State freely (7)
16 Destroyed (6)
18 Discussion (6)
19 Shy (5)
21 Price (4)

Across

1 Prizes (6)

5 Debris (6)

8 Cut very short (of hair) (4)

9 Engravings (8)

10 Flightless birds (5)

11 Calamity (7)

14 Economical (4-9)

16 Pretended (7)

18 Buffalo (5)

20 Struggle helplessly (8)

22 Lock lips (4)

23 Wound together (6)

24 Flower arrangements (6)

Down

2 Causing distress (9)

3 Redecorate (7)

4 Slanting; crooked (4)

5 Woodwind instrument (8)

6 Come with (5)

7 Carry a heavy object (3)

12 Cunningly (9)

13 Upset; hurt (8)

15 Opposite of thinner (7)

17 Particle that holds quarks together (5)

19 Greek god of war (4)

21 Legal rule (3)

CROSSWORD 277

Across

1 Divide into two parts (6)
4 Avoiding waste; thrifty (6)
9 Fast musical composition (7)
10 Mischievous (7)
11 Agree or correspond (5)
12 Mingle with something else (5)
14 Magical incantation (5)
15 Out of fashion (5)
17 Rouses from sleep (5)
18 Back up (7)
20 Stern (7)
21 Applauds (6)
22 Has confidence in (6)

Down

1 Harasses; hems in (6)
2 Learned people (8)
3 Spiced dish (5)
5 Rebuttal (7)
6 Flow copiously (4)
7 Voice box (6)
8 US politician (11)
13 Humility (8)
14 Type of conference (7)
15 Meal eaten in the fresh air (6)
16 Willow twigs (6)
17 Smarter (5)
19 Not any of (4)

Across

1 Flying (8)

5 Superhero film based on comic characters (1-3)

9 Rogue; scoundrel (5)

10 Ship frames (5)

11 Believing (a lie) (10)

14 Astonished (6)

15 Easily handled (6)

17 Study of earthquakes (10)

20 Grumble (5)

21 Trail (5)

22 Prophet (4)

23 Lightest element (8)

Down

1 Ancient boats (4)

2 Derive the benefits (4)

3 Irresistible (12)

4 That is to say (6)

6 Increase greatly in number (8)

7 Bouquets (8)

8 Small meteor (8,4)

12 Minced meat products (8)

13 Short negligee (8)

16 Awkward in movement (6)

18 Noise an explosion makes (4)

19 This covers your body (4)

CROSSWORD 279

Across

1 Recess (6)
4 Structure spanning a river (6)
9 Device for cooling (7)
10 Connected by kinship (7)
11 Brushed clean (5)
12 Managed to deal with something (5)
14 The prevailing fashion (5)
15 Assess; rank (5)
17 Balance (5)
18 Deadlock (7)
20 Not anything (7)
21 Evil spirits (6)
22 Desire for water (6)

Down

1 Right to enter (6)
2 Standards (8)
3 Personal attendant (5)
5 Provide a substitute for (7)
6 Song by two people (4)
7 Dodged (6)
8 Rent manager (anag.) (11)
13 Peacemaker (8)
14 Variant of a thing (7)
15 Showed around (6)
16 Measure of heaviness (6)
17 Piece of land (5)
19 Curl one's hair (4)

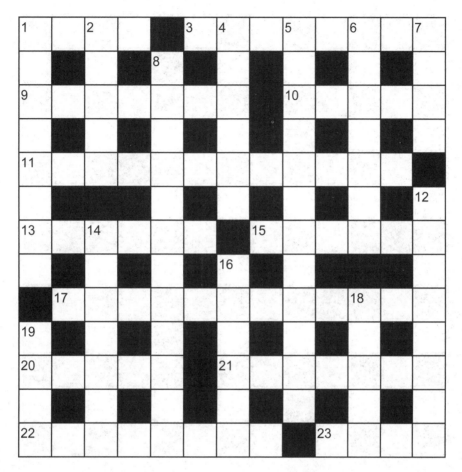

Across

1 Men (4)
3 Not usual (8)
9 E.g. Usain Bolt (7)
10 Fertile area in the desert (5)
11 Commensurate (12)
13 Hire for work (6)
15 Fleet of ships (6)
17 Advance payment (12)
20 Hawaiian greeting (5)
21 Visibly anxious (7)
22 Individuality (8)
23 Backbone; fortitude (4)

Down

1 Wrestled (8)
2 Loutish person (5)
4 A score (6)
5 Cameraperson (12)
6 Plant with starchy tuberous roots (7)
7 Unsure where one is (4)
8 Medicine taken when blocked-up (12)
12 Glove (8)
14 Simple sugar (7)
16 Financial gain (6)
18 Conclude; deduce (5)
19 Hired form of transport (4)

CROSSWORD 281

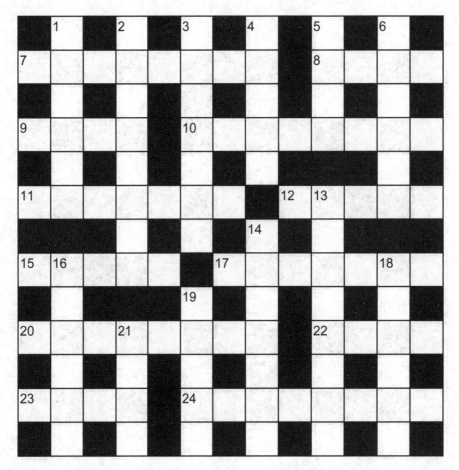

Across

7 Able to feel things (8)
8 Breezy (4)
9 Word that identifies a thing (4)
10 Grow in number (8)
11 Respects (7)
12 Lift up (5)
15 Blocks a hole (5)
17 Concoction (7)
20 Symmetrical open plane curve (8)
22 Created (4)
23 Dare (anag.) (4)
24 Sell at a lower price (8)

Down

1 Further-reaching than (6)
2 Impeding growth (8)
3 Bring and hand over (7)
4 Block of wood (5)
5 Area of a church (4)
6 Outer parts of bread loaves (6)
13 Get the better of through being clever (8)
14 Magicians (7)
16 Hired out (6)
18 Element discovered by Marie and Pierre Curie (6)
19 Position or point (5)
21 Helps (4)

Across

7 Slander (6)

8 Factory siren (6)

9 Abound (4)

10 Starchy banana-like fruit (8)

11 Disperse (7)

13 Sets of two things (5)

15 Lacking interest (5)

16 Went to see (7)

18 Military equipment (8)

19 Duration (4)

21 Turned from liquid to gas (6)

22 Optical phenomenon (6)

Down

1 Very strong wind (4)

2 Completely (opposed) (13)

3 Broke suddenly (7)

4 Cereal plant (5)

5 Mutually inconsistent (13)

6 Pure-bred (of an animal) (8)

12 Internet meeting place (4,4)

14 People harmed by criminal acts (7)

17 Curves (5)

20 Wizard (4)

CROSSWORD 283

Across

1 Low in pitch (4)
3 Bowed to royalty (8)
9 Cautious (7)
10 Basic units of chemical elements (5)
11 Join together as one (5)
12 Leave quickly and in secret (7)
13 Write a music score (6)
15 Swiss city (6)
17 Organic solvent (7)
18 Early version of a document (5)
20 Cake decoration (5)
21 Sprinting (7)
22 Opposite of positive (8)
23 Second-hand (4)

Down

1 Instructions provided with a product (13)
2 Mistake (5)
4 Remove goods from a van (6)
5 Exceptional (12)
6 Form of an element (7)
7 Deprived (13)
8 Reconsideration; item added later (12)
14 Abounding (7)
16 History play by Shakespeare (5,1)
19 Goodbye (Spanish) (5)

Across

1 Garment for the foot (4)
3 Hitting hard (8)
9 Instructor (7)
10 Exams (5)
11 In a hostile manner (12)
13 Generic term for a martial art (4,2)
15 Not written in any key (of music) (6)
17 Developmental (12)
20 Lentil or chickpea (5)
21 A placeholder name (2-3-2)
22 Re-evaluate (8)
23 Plant stalk (4)

Down

1 Events that hinder progress (8)
2 Loud resonant noise (5)
4 Pester (6)
5 Inspiring action (12)
6 Pancreatic hormone (7)
7 Core meaning (4)
8 Happiness (12)
12 Recreational area for children (8)
14 Short story (7)
16 Stagnation or inactivity (6)
18 Detailed assessment of accounts (5)
19 Goad on (4)

CROSSWORD 285

Across

1 Locates or places (5)
4 Defeated heavily (7)
7 Turns over (5)
8 Imitates (8)
9 Shallow food containers (5)
11 Pulling against resistance (8)
15 Disordered state of mind (8)
17 Brusque (5)
19 Country in Africa (8)
20 Pertaining to the voice (5)
21 Intrinsic nature (7)
22 Harsh and grating in sound (5)

Down

1 Dispersing (9)
2 Nominal (7)
3 Thin and bony (7)
4 Meet or find by chance (4,2)
5 Sweltering (6)
6 Not containing anything (5)
10 Apparently (9)
12 Impure acetic acid (7)
13 Type of cell division (7)
14 Erase a mark from a surface (6)
16 Pass (of time) (6)
18 Public disturbances (5)

Across

1 Potential (11)
9 Loosen up (5)
10 State (3)
11 Increment (5)
12 Freight (5)
13 In these times (8)
16 Overly concerned with detail (8)
18 Musical sounds (5)
21 Oak tree nut (5)
22 Domestic bovine animal (3)
23 Submerged ridges of rock (5)
24 Set a limit on (4,3,4)

Down

2 Critiques (7)
3 Distributes around (7)
4 Expression of praise (6)
5 Poisonous (5)
6 Helmet part for protecting the face (5)
7 Science of building aircraft (11)
8 Relating to fireworks (11)
14 Sunshade (7)
15 Piece of furniture (7)
17 Entangle (6)
19 More recent (5)
20 Type of small fastener (5)

CROSSWORD 287

Across

1 Blush (6)
5 Appease (6)
8 Incline (4)
9 Burbling (8)
10 Leader or ruler (5)
11 Medieval military expedition (7)
14 Unexpected (13)
16 Narrow strip of land (7)
18 Percussion instruments (5)
20 Grammatical case (8)
22 Sequence of concentric circles (4)
23 Sculptured figure (6)
24 Vocalist (6)

Down

2 Mammals with trunks (9)
3 Underground prison cell (7)
4 Near (4)
5 Picture of a person (8)
6 Young male horses (5)
7 Fish appendage (3)
12 Trancelike (9)
13 Statuette (8)
15 E.g. from Ethiopia (7)
17 Vital organ (5)
19 Female chickens (4)
21 Nevertheless (3)

Across

1 Sunshades (8)
5 Deficiency (4)
8 Cancel (5)
9 Insanitary (7)
10 Lifted (7)
12 People who insist on sticking to formal rules (7)
14 Root vegetables (7)
16 Currents of air (7)
18 Live in (7)
19 Derogatory in an indirect way (5)
20 Movable barrier (4)
21 Recent arrival (8)

Down

1 Sweet juicy fruit (4)
2 Leased (6)
3 Seriousness (9)
4 Giggles (6)
6 Representatives (6)
7 Royal domains (8)
11 Inherent (9)
12 Baffling (8)
13 Outcome (6)
14 Insect that transmits sleeping sickness (6)
15 Weak through age or illness (6)
17 Mammal that may have antlers (4)

CROSSWORD 289

Across

1 Become part of a solution (8)
5 Scarpered (4)
9 Female relatives (5)
10 Dislikes intensely (5)
11 Going under water (10)
14 Standard; usual (6)
15 Make a bubbling sound (6)
17 Punctuation mark (10)
20 Repasts (5)
21 Foot joint (5)
22 Moral obligation (4)
23 Shouted very loudly (8)

Down

1 Clock face (4)
2 Male children (4)
3 Obfuscation (12)
4 Measure of loudness (6)
6 Settling (anag.) (8)
7 Creator (8)
8 Street (12)
12 Not injured (8)
13 Conceited (8)
16 Picture produced from many small pieces (6)
18 Read quickly (4)
19 Nourishes (4)

Across

1 Robust (6)
5 E.g. use a chair (3)
7 Tidily kept (5)
8 Secret affair (7)
9 Ensnares (5)
10 Impartial parties (8)
12 Take away (6)
14 Cosmetics (4-2)
17 Trestles (anag.) (8)
18 Round steering device (5)
20 Electronic retention of data (7)
21 Small house (5)
22 24-hour period (3)
23 Sagacious (6)

Down

2 Ancient warship (7)
3 Show to be false (8)
4 Leave out (4)
5 Odd (7)
6 Type of dance (3-4)
7 Went down on one knee (5)
11 Careful (8)
12 Huge coniferous tree (7)
13 Stingy (7)
15 Standing erect (7)
16 Stop (5)
19 Vein of metal ore (4)

CROSSWORD 291

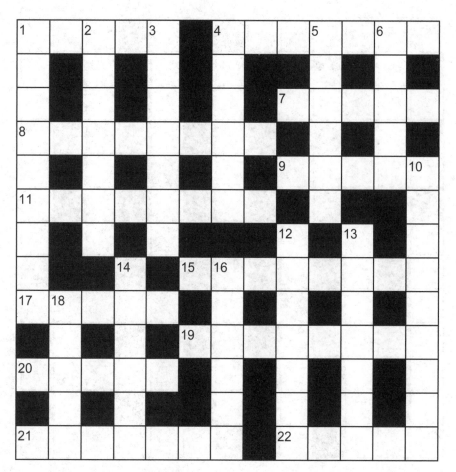

Across

1 Packs tightly (5)
4 Anthropoid (7)
7 Impossible to see round (of a bend) (5)
8 Whipped (8)
9 Domineering (5)
11 Breed of retriever (8)
15 Believed to be true (8)
17 Retail establishments (5)
19 Deeply respectful (8)
20 E.g. an orange (5)
21 Fugitive (7)
22 Streamlined (5)

Down

1 Incessant (9)
2 Takes in (7)
3 Bizarre (7)
4 Get by with what is available (4,2)
5 Move with a bounding motion (6)
6 Types (5)
10 Criterion (9)
12 Imperfections (7)
13 Tall tower (7)
14 Top aim (anag.) (6)
16 Compel by intimidation (6)
18 Lyres (5)

Across

1 Subtle variation (6)
5 Top (anag.) (3)
7 Moves on foot (5)
8 Charismatic person (7)
9 Barks (5)
10 Flower sellers (8)
12 Shun (6)
14 Not impartial (6)
17 Free from sensual desire (8)
18 Ciphers (5)
20 Provided with food and drink (7)
21 Smug smile (5)
22 Nevertheless (3)
23 Small stones (6)

Down

2 Confirms a decision; supports (7)
3 Grouped together (8)
4 Imperfection (4)
5 Diffusion of molecules through a membrane (7)
6 Gnarled (7)
7 Penned (5)
11 Ruler who is unconstrained by law (8)
12 Precisely (7)
13 Least warm (7)
15 Wicked look that causes harm (4,3)
16 Bird sound (5)
19 Slender (4)

CROSSWORD 293

Across

7 Show-off (6)
8 Desiring food (6)
9 High-pitched noise (4)
10 Sports grounds (8)
11 Group of five (7)
13 Animal enclosures (5)
15 Brilliant and clear (5)
16 At a greater distance (7)
18 Intended to appeal to ordinary people (8)
19 Actor's part in a film (4)
21 Set out on a journey (6)
22 Damp and sticky to touch (6)

Down

1 Garden watering device (4)
2 Upright; vertical (13)
3 Furnishes with pasture (7)
4 Bottle (5)
5 Destroying microorganisms (13)
6 First public performance (8)
12 Specified work outfits (8)
14 Moral rightness (7)
17 Passes the tongue over (5)
20 Calcium compound; fruit (4)

Across

1 Chess piece (6)
7 Surpass in excellence (8)
8 What our planet orbits (3)
9 Writhe (6)
10 Unwell (4)
11 Use inefficiently; rubbish (5)
13 Ate quickly (7)
15 Nasal opening (7)
17 Simple aquatic plants (5)
21 In a good way (4)
22 Winged child (6)
23 Negligent (3)
24 Discard; abandon (8)
25 Reigns (anag.) (6)

Down

1 Confer (6)
2 Detects; feels (6)
3 City-state in ancient Greece (5)
4 Organ of digestion (7)
5 Heavenly (8)
6 The spirit or soul (6)
12 Entirety (8)
14 Rayon fabric (7)
16 Complied with orders (6)
18 Bad-tempered mythical creature (6)
19 Magical potion (6)
20 Green vegetables (5)

CROSSWORD 295

Across

7 Process food (6)

8 Gained deservedly (6)

9 Accomplishment (4)

10 Act of treachery (8)

11 Compels (7)

13 Haggard (5)

15 Factual evidence (5)

16 People who rule (7)

18 Dismiss as unimportant (5,3)

19 Tear down (4)

21 State of the USA (6)

22 Character created by Charles M. Schulz (6)

Down

1 Bog (4)

2 Voice projection artist (13)

3 Buildings for horses (7)

4 Trivial (5)

5 Simple problem-solving method (5,3,5)

6 Rain tree (anag.) (8)

12 Anniversary of when you are born (8)

14 Concerned just with oneself (7)

17 Brag (5)

20 Moves speedily (4)

Across

1 Cuts slightly (5)
4 Taking a break (7)
7 Is scared of (5)
8 Throaty (of a speech sound) (8)
9 Type of plastic; record (5)
11 Provoking (8)
15 Relations by blood (8)
17 Floating platforms (5)
19 Relating to office work (8)
20 Printed publications (5)
21 Deprived of food (7)
22 Charming and elegant (5)

Down

1 Less well behaved (9)
2 Map line showing equal height (7)
3 Build in a certain place (7)
4 Keep hold of (6)
5 Long essay (6)
6 Anxious (5)
10 Doppelganger (9)
12 Fish-eating birds of prey (7)
13 Musical composition (7)
14 Stroke (anag.) (6)
16 Away from the coast (6)
18 Currently in progress (5)

CROSSWORD 297

Across

1 E.g. monkey or whale (6)
5 Pop music performance (3)
7 Vast multitude (5)
8 French dance (7)
9 Type of herring (5)
10 Monumental Egyptian structures (8)
12 Begins (6)
14 Ancient Persian king (6)
17 Work surface (8)
18 Fluffy and soft (5)
20 Chocolate chewy cake (7)
21 Small streams (5)
22 Performed an action (3)
23 Time of life when one is old (6)

Down

2 Someone who studies data (7)
3 Tries (8)
4 Weapons (4)
5 Transmission (7)
6 Troughs that carry rainwater (7)
7 Shade (anag.) (5)
11 Prosperous; wealthy (4-2-2)
12 Burdened (7)
13 Causing difficulty (7)
15 Wearing away (7)
16 Wounding remarks (5)
19 Ivy League university (4)

Across

1 Legal soundness (8)

5 Move fast in a straight line (4)

9 Drenches (5)

10 Breathing organs (5)

11 Insecurity (10)

14 Set free or release (6)

15 Leave (6)

17 Beyond the scope of scientific understanding (10)

20 Causes great damage (5)

21 Maw (5)

22 Heroic tale (4)

23 Porch (8)

Down

1 Container for flowers (4)

2 A hole that lets liquid escape (4)

3 Clarity (12)

4 Inside information (3-3)

6 Church rules (5,3)

7 Cuts into bits (8)

8 Heavy long-handled tool (12)

12 Assists; holds up (8)

13 Frightening (8)

16 Small cave (6)

18 Search for (4)

19 Counter used in poker (4)

Across

1 Policy of direct action (8)
5 Decorated a cake (4)
8 Use to one's advantage (5)
9 Newsworthy (7)
10 Helps to happen (7)
12 Hawker (7)
14 Trembles (7)
16 Envisage (7)
18 Plans to do something (7)
19 Brought forth (5)
20 Spiritual teacher (4)
21 Took in (8)

Down

1 First man (4)
2 Made fun of (6)
3 Worthless (9)
4 Wrongdoer (6)
6 Small round stone (6)
7 Kitchen sideboards (8)
11 Sensible (9)
12 Trifling (8)
13 Cheese shredder (6)
14 E.g. spring or winter (6)
15 Liveliness (6)
17 Main acting part (4)

Across

1 From a distance (4)
3 Fierce contest (8)
9 Country in the West Indies (7)
10 Vertical part of a step (5)
11 Strange and mysterious (5)
12 Shoulder blade (7)
13 Set fire to (6)
15 Stick to (6)
17 Of great size (7)
18 Capital of Vietnam (5)
20 E.g. Pacific or Atlantic (5)
21 Dwelling (7)
22 Anxious uncertainty (8)
23 Extremely (4)

Down

1 Shortened forms of words (13)
2 Loathe (5)
4 Be preoccupied with something (6)
5 Pungent gas used as a preservative (12)
6 Movement conveying an expression (7)
7 Menacingly (13)
8 Impudence (12)
14 Chats (7)
16 Rebukes angrily (6)
19 Foolishly credulous (5)

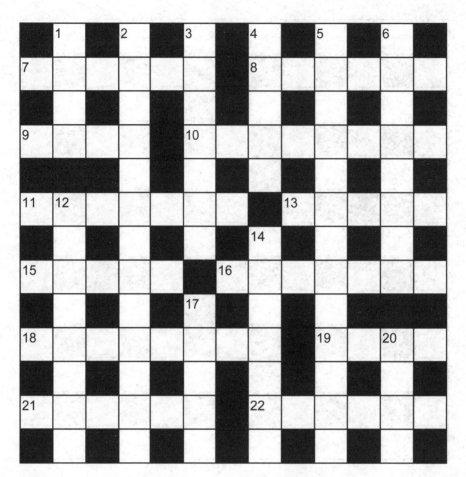

Across

7 Type of canoe (6)

8 Amount of money left in a will (6)

9 Touched (4)

10 Thinks deeply about (8)

11 Gadgets (7)

13 Follows closely (5)

15 Contrapuntal composition (5)

16 Cowardly (7)

18 Object that gives out heat (8)

19 Irritates constantly (4)

21 Brandy (6)

22 Church services (6)

Down

1 Sixth month of the year (4)

2 Things that are given (13)

3 Began (7)

4 Precipice (5)

5 Pleasantness (13)

6 Coal containers (8)

12 Imitator (8)

14 Most important (7)

17 Slender piece of wood (5)

20 Increased in size (4)

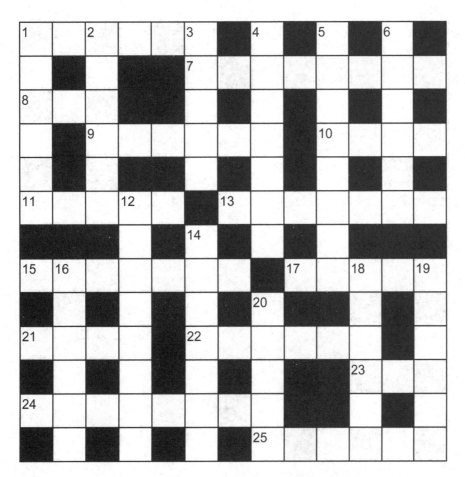

Across

1 Assumed propositions (6)
7 Assembles (8)
8 Not on (3)
9 Animal used to catch rabbits (6)
10 Wild mountain goat (4)
11 Relating to the kidneys (5)
13 Left out (7)
15 Run with light steps (7)
17 Oppress grievously (5)
21 Barrier between rooms (4)
22 Rejoices (6)
23 Slip up (3)
24 Each tour (anag.) (8)
25 Young people (6)

Down

1 Pillager (6)
2 Small cake (6)
3 Open disrespect (5)
4 Former (3-4)
5 Negotiator (8)
6 Tranquil (6)
12 Fans (8)
14 More than two (7)
16 Early spring flower (6)
18 Cause to fall from a horse (6)
19 Card game similar to whist (6)
20 Pulpy (5)

CROSSWORD 303

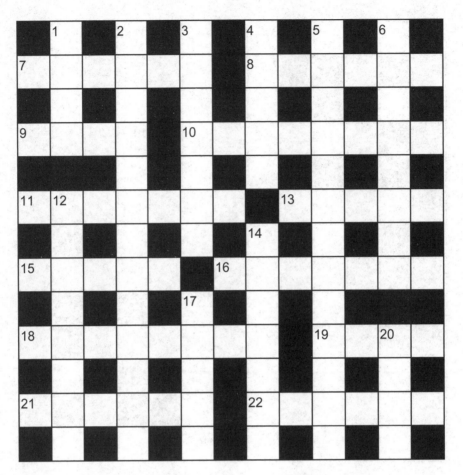

Across

7 Nearer in the future (6)
8 Public speaker (6)
9 Smile broadly (4)
10 Decorative designs (8)
11 Strut about (7)
13 Handle a tool effectively (5)
15 Shared by two or more people (5)
16 Land depressions (7)
18 Person who makes arrows (8)
19 Put in order (4)
21 Cry and sniffle (6)
22 Ascends (6)

Down

1 Deep affection (4)
2 Uninventive (13)
3 Set of three things (7)
4 Pillars (5)
5 Desiring worldly possessions (13)
6 Understate (8)
12 Forest (8)
14 Jeer noisily at (7)
17 White soft limestone (5)
20 Applies friction to (4)

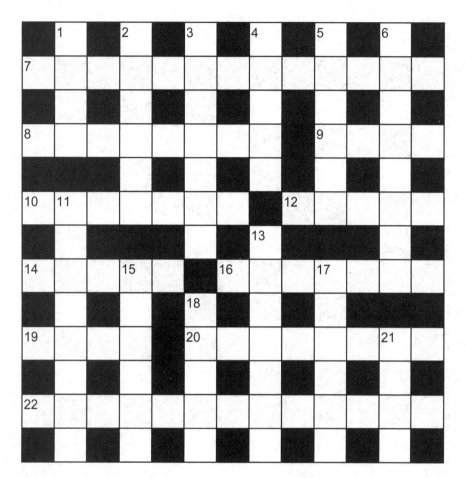

Across

7 Resonance (13)
8 Move to another country (8)
9 Pull a sulky face (4)
10 Cheer (7)
12 Action words (5)
14 Empty area; gap (5)
16 Ship worker (7)
19 Small body of water (4)
20 Point of contact; masonry support (8)
22 State of extreme happiness (7,6)

Down

1 Microscopic organism (4)
2 Act of union (6)
3 Wears away (7)
4 Short and sweet (5)
5 Document fastener (6)
6 State capital of South Carolina (8)
11 Blows up (8)
13 Bad-tempered (7)
15 Visitor to your door (6)
17 Burrowing marsupial (6)
18 Oily; greasy (5)
21 Require (4)

CROSSWORD 305

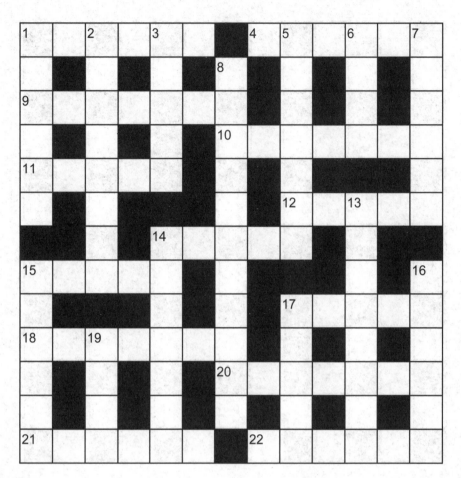

Across

1 Conform (6)
4 Type of muscle (6)
9 Squirm (7)
10 Tranquil (7)
11 Religious acts (5)
12 Venomous snake (5)
14 Legend (5)
15 Foreign language (informal) (5)
17 Panorama (5)
18 Type of diving (4,3)
20 Weaves; clothing (7)
21 Cease (6)
22 Agreement (6)

Down

1 Escrow (anag.) (6)
2 Preserve (8)
3 Company emblems (5)
5 Difficult to catch (7)
6 Ride the waves (4)
7 Long swelling wave (6)
8 Walk round a place (11)
13 Convince (8)
14 Remains of living things (7)
15 Lived with as a guest (6)
16 Breed of hound (6)
17 Infective agent (5)
19 Hens lay these (4)

Across

1 Risky (6)

5 Amp (anag.) (3)

7 Reproductive unit of fungi (5)

8 As fast as possible (4,3)

9 Explosive devices (5)

10 Inattentively; vaguely (8)

12 The rear parts of ships (6)

14 Flat-bottomed boats (6)

17 System of conduct and values (8)

18 Hard outgrowths on animals (5)

20 Immature fruit of a cucumber (7)

21 Giggle (5)

22 Possessed (3)

23 Tricky question (6)

Down

2 Large marine flatfish (7)

3 Coronation ceremony (8)

4 Computer virus (4)

5 Significance (7)

6 Have (7)

7 Took illegally (5)

11 E.g. from Tokyo (8)

12 Very great (3-4)

13 Green gemstone (7)

15 Wind together (7)

16 Expel air abruptly (5)

19 Not sweet (4)

CROSSWORD 307

Across

1 Parrot sound (6)
7 Words representing numbers (8)
8 Auction offer (3)
9 Joined together (6)
10 Dons (anag.) (4)
11 Purchaser (5)
13 Brings to effective action (7)
15 Sticks to (7)
17 Worries (5)
21 Unit of power (4)
22 Pedant (6)
23 Witch (3)
24 The day after today (8)
25 Predatory marine fish (pl.) (6)

Down

1 Residential district (6)
2 Excessively (6)
3 Speed in nautical miles per hour (5)
4 Smears (7)
5 Grainy (8)
6 Willingly (6)
12 Negatively charged particle (8)
14 Aides (7)
16 Ordained minister (6)
18 One or the other of two (6)
19 Marsh plants (6)
20 Makes beer (5)

Across

1 Daring (4)

3 Busy (8)

9 Got too big for something (7)

10 E.g. mallards (5)

11 Organ of sight (3)

12 Solid blow (5)

13 Evade (5)

15 Prevent (5)

17 Twelve (5)

18 Female pronoun (3)

19 Hackneyed (5)

20 Sailing ship (7)

21 Thing serving as an appropriate model (8)

22 Capture a piece in chess (4)

Down

1 Capable of being decomposed (13)

2 Machine for shaping wood or metal (5)

4 One who lacks courage (6)

5 Not discernible (12)

6 Have as a part (7)

7 Act of vanishing (13)

8 A type of error in speech (8,4)

14 Medicated tablet (7)

16 Mystery; riddle (6)

18 Doglike mammal (5)

Across

1 Built (11)
9 Ire (5)
10 Knock vigorously (3)
11 Dreadful (5)
12 Intense light beam (5)
13 Antique; obsolete (8)
16 News journalist (8)
18 Daisy-like flower (5)
21 Third Greek letter (5)
22 Bottle top (3)
23 Customary practice (5)
24 Devices popular before computers existed (11)

Down

2 Sets of clothes (7)
3 Lacking depth (7)
4 System of doing things (6)
5 Christmas song (5)
6 Gets through merit (5)
7 Inescapable (11)
8 Fitting (11)
14 Opposite of shortest (7)
15 Speak haltingly (7)
17 Cream pastry (6)
19 Toy bear (5)
20 Path or road (5)

Across

1 Award (informal) (4)

3 Musical pieces for solo instruments (8)

9 Framework (7)

10 Send money in payment (5)

11 Set of moral principles (5)

12 Feeling of hopelessness (7)

13 Jesting (6)

15 Remains of a fire (6)

17 Establishment for making beer (7)

18 Japanese dish (5)

20 Lawful (5)

21 Imposing a tax (7)

22 Speed up (8)

23 Unattractive (4)

Down

1 50th anniversary of a major event (6,7)

2 Incision; indent (5)

4 Exaggerate (6)

5 24th December (9,3)

6 Search through (7)

7 Fascinatingly (13)

8 Unhappy (12)

14 Patella (7)

16 Small hole (6)

19 Smart; hurt (5)

CROSSWORD 311

Across

1 Intrigue (8)
5 Cat sound (4)
8 Memos (5)
9 Process of setting something in motion (5-2)
10 Follow a winding course (of a river) (7)
12 Flower-shaped competition award (7)
14 Poured with rain (7)
16 Clear perception (7)
18 Meaninglessness (7)
19 Redden (5)
20 Deities (4)
21 Taught (8)

Down

1 Public houses (4)
2 Teachers (6)
3 Holding out against (9)
4 Plant with oil rich seeds (6)
6 Not arranged neatly (6)
7 Gave an account of (8)
11 Occurring without oxygen (9)
12 Living in (8)
13 E.g. Borneo (6)
14 Steady (anag.) (6)
15 Uproar (6)
17 Country bordered by Libya and Sudan (4)

Across

1 Insubstantial; breakable (6)
5 Relieve or free from (3)
7 Objection (5)
8 Unfamiliar (7)
9 Secret agents (5)
10 Haunches of a horse (8)
12 Leave the nest (6)
14 Unit of astronomical length (6)
17 Icy natal (anag.) (8)
18 Shaped up (5)
20 Understood (7)
21 Female horses (5)
22 Hit high into the air (3)
23 Goes round the edge of; garments (6)

Down

2 Pertaining to the tongue (7)
3 Paucity (8)
4 Tears open (4)
5 Studies for an exam (7)
6 Severe (7)
7 Knotty protuberance on a tree (5)
11 Distinctive feature (8)
12 Numbers from 50 to 59 (7)
13 Efficiency (7)
15 Plain and clear (7)
16 Unexpected catches (5)
19 Dreadful (4)

CROSSWORD 313

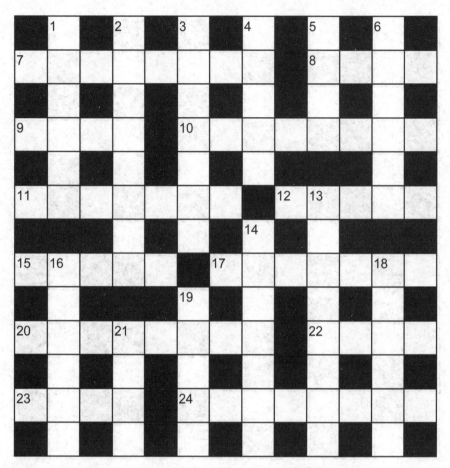

Across

7 Bog (8)
8 Period of seven days (4)
9 In case (4)
10 Grew in size (8)
11 Non-professional (7)
12 Salad plant (5)
15 Dizzy (5)
17 Foundation garments (7)
20 Changing gradually (8)
22 Small metal spike (4)
23 Sent by (4)
24 Act of hard work (8)

Down

1 Building exhibiting objects (6)
2 Excited or annoyed (8)
3 Jumbled (5-2)
4 Retains (5)
5 White aquatic bird (4)
6 Cuts off (6)
13 Evoke memories (8)
14 Eye protectors (7)
16 Turn upside down (6)
18 Garment maker (6)
19 Quoted (5)
21 Compact mass (4)

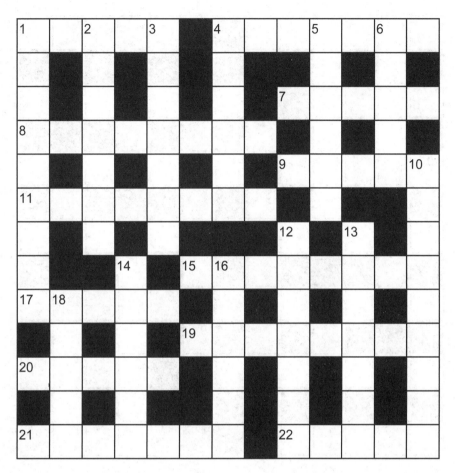

Across

1 Creator (5)
4 Inclination (7)
7 Device used to sharpen razors (5)
8 Deny (8)
9 Horse carts (5)
11 Qualified for entry (8)
15 Large Spanish estate (8)
17 Amphibians (5)
19 Assimilate again (8)
20 Put a question to (5)
21 Complex wholes (7)
22 Role; office (5)

Down

1 Intermediary (9)
2 Affinity (7)
3 Get back (7)
4 Positioned in the middle (6)
5 Puts off (6)
6 Thermosetting resin (5)
10 Item worn by a tennis player (9)
12 Small apes (7)
13 Swell with fluid (7)
14 Thoroughfare (6)
16 Modifies (6)
18 Piece of writing (5)

CROSSWORD 315

Across

1 Jumped up (6)
5 Ignores completely (6)
8 Brown seaweed (4)
9 Prevent heat loss (8)
10 Army rank (5)
11 Humorous; done in fun (7)
14 Connections or associations (13)
16 Idealistic (7)
18 Edward ___ : English composer (5)
20 Substance used for polishing (8)
22 Very small (4)
23 Snake (6)
24 Fast-flowing part of a river (6)

Down

2 Widespread (9)
3 Ancient large storage jar (7)
4 Harsh and miserable (4)
5 Boundary mark of a tennis court (8)
6 Metallic compound (5)
7 Clothing needed for an activity (3)
12 Unintentional (9)
13 Quotation (8)
15 Summit (7)
17 Soft fruit (5)
19 Ale (4)
21 Young male (3)

Across

7 Autonomous (4-9)
8 Strive (8)
9 Cease (4)
10 Horse's fodder container (7)
12 Instruct (5)
14 Long wooden seat (5)
16 Midday meals (7)
19 Strong and healthy (4)
20 On a higher floor (8)
22 The first and last (5,3,5)

Down

1 Hit hard (4)
2 Exude (6)
3 Curdle (7)
4 Humorous images that spread rapidly online (5)
5 One of a kind (6)
6 Surround (8)
11 Protective garments (8)
13 Grant (7)
15 Type of nursery (6)
17 Delights greatly (6)
18 Large American felines (5)
21 Fixes the result (4)

Across

1 Purpose (6)
7 Decreasing (8)
8 Violate a law of God (3)
9 Gaming tile (6)
10 Thug; oaf (4)
11 Exhaust gases (5)
13 Cantered (7)
15 Able to pay one's debts (7)
17 Stage items (5)
21 Hindu spiritual discipline (4)
22 Provoke (6)
23 Blade for rowing a boat (3)
24 Remote; cut off (8)
25 Fills up (6)

Down

1 Stifle (anag.) (6)
2 Type of bicycle (6)
3 Distinguishing characteristic (5)
4 Postpone (7)
5 Person who shapes stone (8)
6 Steep in liquid (6)
12 Arousing jealousy (8)
14 Restlessness; state of worry (7)
16 Musician playing a double-reed instrument (6)
18 Unique (3-3)
19 Keeps (6)
20 Rushes along; skims (5)

Across

1 Harsh (of a place) (11)
9 Pattern (5)
10 Command to a horse (3)
11 Musical compositions (5)
12 Many times (5)
13 Got ready (8)
16 Canine that herds animals (8)
18 Crime of setting something on fire (5)
21 Skirmish (5)
22 Unit of energy (3)
23 Cowboy exhibition (5)
24 Science of communications in living things and machines (11)

Down

2 Subtleties (7)
3 Last longer than (a rival) (7)
4 Where one finds Athens (6)
5 Record on tape (5)
6 Period of darkness (5)
7 Vanished (11)
8 Unintelligible (11)
14 State of the USA (7)
15 Delightful (7)
17 Toughen (6)
19 Wet (5)
20 Boldness; courage (5)

CROSSWORD 319

Across

1 Servings of food (8)
5 Box (4)
8 Giraffes have long ones (5)
9 Containerful (7)
10 Selling (7)
12 Educational establishment (7)
14 Turn aside from a course (7)
16 Ornamental stone openwork (7)
18 Additions to a document (7)
19 All (5)
20 Yellow part of an egg (4)
21 Truly (8)

Down

1 Breathe hard (4)
2 Pull back from (6)
3 Impertinence (9)
4 Indigenous (6)
6 Seabird (6)
7 Demote (8)
11 Confident (9)
12 Opposite in meaning (8)
13 Open type of footwear (6)
14 Extremely energetic person (6)
15 Measure of how strongly an object reflects light (6)
17 Legendary story (4)

Across

1 Alliance (11)
9 Unit of light (5)
10 Came first in a race (3)
11 Drives out from a place (5)
12 Biblical king (5)
13 Shining intensely (8)
16 Conclusive argument (8)
18 Small branch (5)
21 Fill with high spirits (5)
22 Female sheep (3)
23 Machine for making butter (5)
24 Streamlined (11)

Down

2 Unusually large (7)
3 Incorrectly (7)
4 Inhibit (6)
5 Cattle-breeding farm (5)
6 Crouch down in fear (5)
7 Company that transmits TV shows (11)
8 Unintentional (11)
14 Aerial (7)
15 Dry red table wine of Italy (7)
17 State of great comfort (6)
19 Pass a rope through (5)
20 Type of lizard (5)

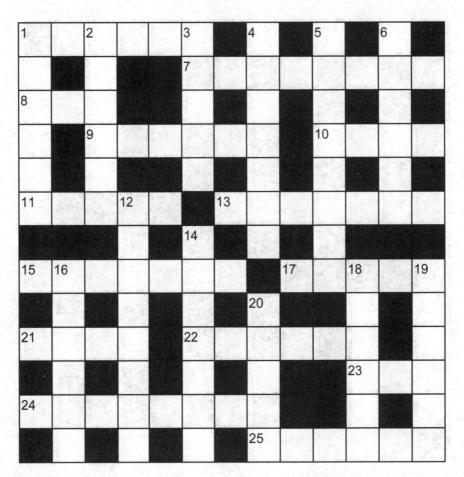

Across

1 E.g. iron and gold (6)
7 Boldly and courageously (8)
8 Silent (3)
9 Extreme confusion (6)
10 Wist (anag.) (4)
11 Woolly ruminant animal (5)
13 Cargo (7)
15 Seems (7)
17 Kind of beet (5)
21 Moist (4)
22 Fierce woman (6)
23 Chatter (3)
24 Representations or descriptions of data (8)
25 Contemporary (6)

Down

1 Copies (6)
2 Topple (6)
3 Petite (5)
4 From now on (7)
5 Be heavier than (8)
6 Malfunction (6)
12 Freed from an obligation (8)
14 Insignificant (7)
16 Caper (6)
18 Point in an orbit furthest from earth (6)
19 Seaport in South Africa (6)
20 Greenish-bronze fish (5)

Across

1 Purchase of a company by another (11)
9 Respected person in a field (5)
10 Grassland (3)
11 Crazy (5)
12 Speed (5)
13 More powerful (8)
16 Exhaustive (8)
18 Keen (5)
21 Collection of maps (5)
22 Shed tears (3)
23 Extra component (3-2)
24 Images recorded on film (11)

Down

2 Apprehend; snare (7)
3 Eternal (7)
4 Obstruct (6)
5 Freshwater food fish (5)
6 Stares at amorously (5)
7 Infinite knowledge (11)
8 Pairs of round brackets (11)
14 Sheer dress fabric (7)
15 Prepare for public consumption (7)
17 Sausage in a roll (3,3)
19 Sculptured symbol (5)
20 Respond to (5)

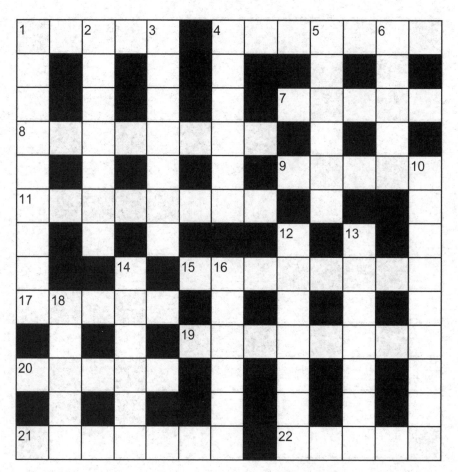

Across

1 Hints (anag.) (5)
4 Maxims (7)
7 Discard (5)
8 Small North Atlantic fish (8)
9 Waterway (5)
11 Young plant (8)
15 Worldwide outbreak (8)
17 Competed in a speed contest (5)
19 Retrieve a file from the internet (8)
20 Aperture in the eye (5)
21 Flowering shrubs (7)
22 Sound of an emergency vehicle (5)

Down

1 Period of three months (9)
2 Frozen water spears (7)
3 Affectionately (7)
4 Mirthless (6)
5 Becomes subject to (6)
6 Eat grass (5)
10 Very low (of a price) (5-4)
12 Strangeness (7)
13 Give authority to (7)
14 Antenna (6)
16 Takes up (6)
18 Humming (5)

Across

1 Examine in detail (11)
9 Individual things (5)
10 Half of four (3)
11 Scope or extent (5)
12 Produce as a fruit (5)
13 Most precipitous (8)
16 Bring together (8)
18 Brings up (5)
21 Performing a deed (5)
22 Ovoid foodstuff (3)
23 Approaches (5)
24 Switched off (11)

Down

2 Takes small bites (7)
3 Statement of commemoration (7)
4 Pinches sharply (6)
5 Blowing in puffs (of wind) (5)
6 Levy (5)
7 Moved to another place (11)
8 Bird of prey (6,5)
14 Salt lake in the Jordan valley (4,3)
15 Shorten (7)
17 Highly seasoned sausage (6)
19 Standpoint (5)
20 Pertaining to sound (5)

CROSSWORD 325

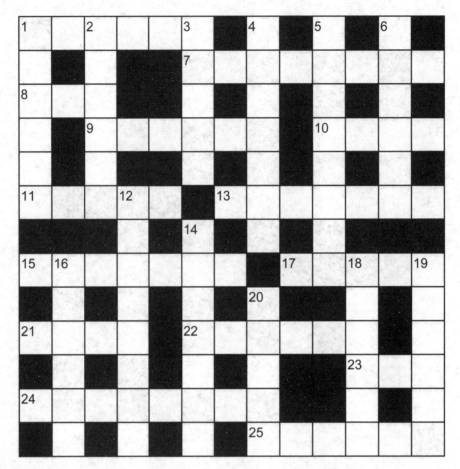

Across

1 Where one finds Quebec (6)
7 Absurd (8)
8 Widely cultivated cereal grass (3)
9 Tracks (6)
10 Pairs (4)
11 Bad-tempered (5)
13 Regain strength (7)
15 Receiver (7)
17 Pastime (5)
21 Playing cards (4)
22 Refrigerator compartment; old-fashioned refrigerator (6)
23 Not near (3)
24 Fact of being irreversible (8)
25 Soup spoons (6)

Down

1 Shuts (6)
2 Talk idly (6)
3 Attach (5)
4 Dons clothes (7)
5 Person highly skilled in music (8)
6 In abundance (6)
12 Guiding principle (8)
14 Excess of liabilities over assets (7)
16 Greek mathematician (6)
18 Containerful (6)
19 Hankers after (6)
20 Precious stone (5)

Across

1 Reflection of sound (4)
3 Occasional (8)
9 Salad plant (7)
10 Lesser (5)
11 Customary (5)
12 Fruitful; inventive (7)
13 Single-celled organism (6)
15 Closely held back (4-2)
17 Exertions (7)
18 Unfasten a garment (5)
20 Expel (5)
21 Increase in size (7)
22 Teaching (8)
23 Stimulate the appetite (4)

Down

1 Expression of approval (13)
2 Type of poem (5)
4 Bribe (6)
5 Regretfully (12)
6 Stinted (anag.) (7)
7 Person who writes letters regularly (13)
8 Fellow plotter (12)
14 Unconventional (7)
16 Toward the rear of a ship (6)
19 Roost (5)

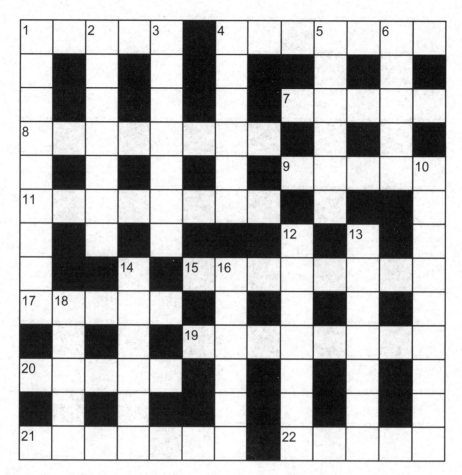

Across

1 Speaks (5)
4 Portable lamp (7)
7 Appears (5)
8 Visitors to a place (8)
9 Spore (anag.) (5)
11 Illuminating (8)
15 Orange pigment found in carrots (8)
17 Sharp peak (5)
19 Forbearing (8)
20 Chairs (5)
21 Assign (7)
22 Committee (5)

Down

1 Insipid and bland (9)
2 Form of public worship (7)
3 Sum of human conditions (7)
4 Pay attention to what is said (6)
5 Speculative view (6)
6 Slopes (5)
10 Indispensable (9)
12 Hide (5-2)
13 Six-sided shape (7)
14 Person gliding on ice (6)
16 Evoke a feeling (6)
18 Earnest appeals (5)

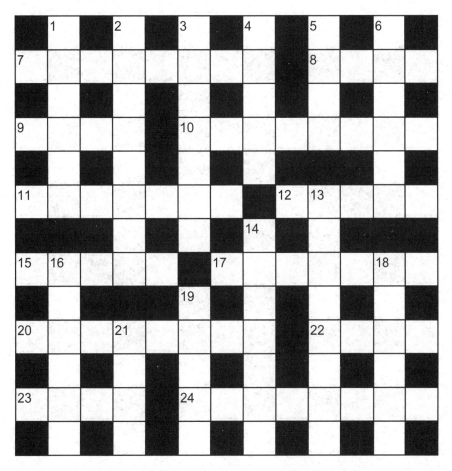

Across

7 Majesty (8)

8 Deceiver (4)

9 Stride; single step (4)

10 Curiosity (8)

11 Pulls back from (7)

12 Internal parasites (5)

15 Ringing sound (5)

17 Remain alive (7)

20 Sport (8)

22 Extreme point (4)

23 Bewilder; stun (4)

24 Eland (8)

Down

1 Mysterious; secret (6)

2 Chamber leading to a larger space (8)

3 Shelters for dogs (7)

4 Outer layer of bread (5)

5 Scheme (4)

6 Payment for the release of someone (6)

13 Something that gets in the way (8)

14 Distinctive attribute (7)

16 Hurrah (6)

18 Drowsy (6)

19 Tokyo's country (5)

21 Extremities of the feet (4)

Across

1 Support or foundation (4)
3 Type of state (8)
9 Elevate (7)
10 Once more (5)
11 Opposite of high (3)
12 Bend or curl (5)
13 Variety or kind (5)
15 Praise highly (5)
17 Stroll casually (5)
18 Sticky substance (3)
19 Medicinal ointment (5)
20 Sickness (7)
21 Ultimate (8)
22 Prestigious TV award (4)

Down

1 Spicy fish stew (13)
2 Spread by scattering (5)
4 Ten plus one (6)
5 Intolerable (12)
6 Departing (7)
7 Prominently (13)
8 Conflict of opinion (12)
14 Anniversary of an event (7)
16 Continent (6)
18 Shine brightly (5)

CROSSWORD 330

Across

7 Benevolent and generous (13)
8 Away from land (8)
9 Fastens a knot (4)
10 Huge (7)
12 Strong gust of wind (5)
14 Treats successfully (5)
16 These aid sight (7)
19 Suffered the consequences (4)
20 Block (8)
22 As another option (13)

Down

1 Cook (4)
2 Advantages (6)
3 Concern; implicate (7)
4 Footwear (pl.) (5)
5 Provider of cheap accommodation (6)
6 Person granted a permit (8)
11 Open to suggestion (8)
13 Small storage rooms or cupboards (7)
15 Shelves (6)
17 Try hard to achieve (6)
18 Strike repeatedly (5)
21 Unorthodox religion or sect (4)

CROSSWORD 331

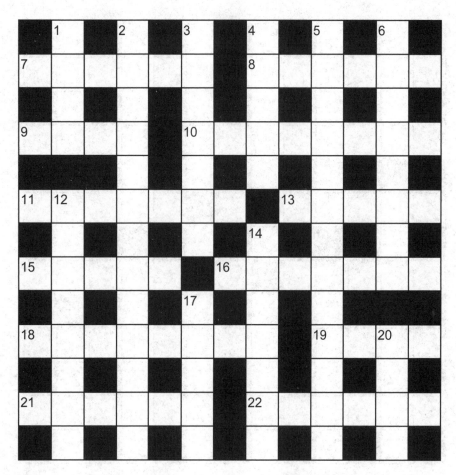

Across

7 Countenance (6)

8 Agricultural implement (6)

9 Coniferous trees of the genus Taxus (4)

10 Have a different opinion (8)

11 Christian ministers (7)

13 Piles (5)

15 Sanctimonious (5)

16 E.g. spring and winter (7)

18 Ability to act as one wishes (4,4)

19 Change (4)

21 Informer (6)

22 Make holy (6)

Down

1 Erase (4)

2 State of the USA (13)

3 Fixing (7)

4 Whip eggs (5)

5 Increasingly (13)

6 Simple and unsophisticated (8)

12 Person who leaves a country (8)

14 In good physical condition (7)

17 Emits a breath of relief (5)

20 Eurasian crow (4)

Across

7 Friendly (13)

8 Sentence sung before a psalm (8)

9 Vessel (4)

10 Cure-alls (7)

12 Principle of conduct (5)

14 Plant stalks (5)

16 Tearing (7)

19 Eager (4)

20 Madly (8)

22 Pictures accompanying text (13)

Down

1 Loose flowing garment (4)

2 Winged monster of Thebes (6)

3 Heavy metal weights (7)

4 Connects (5)

5 Country whose capital is Lusaka (6)

6 German shepherd dog (8)

11 Recently (8)

13 Festivals (7)

15 Resolute or brave (6)

17 Writing implement (6)

18 Tips (5)

21 Elan (anag.) (4)

CROSSWORD 333

Across

1 Incalculable (11)
9 Put into use (5)
10 Part of a curve (3)
11 Employing (5)
12 Harsh and serious in manner (5)
13 Magnitude of a sound (8)
16 Based on reason (8)
18 Large bird of prey (5)
21 Epic poem ascribed to Homer (5)
22 Metric unit of measurement (historical) (3)
23 Not illuminated (5)
24 Basically (11)

Down

2 Harmful (7)
3 Method of presenting a play (7)
4 Urges to do something (6)
5 Bottomless pit (5)
6 Exit (5)
7 Type of triangle (11)
8 Admit to be true (11)
14 Civilians trained as soldiers (7)
15 Rude (7)
17 Charm (6)
19 Narrow valleys (5)
20 Short musical composition (5)

Across

1 Stir up (6)
5 Hearts (anag.) (6)
8 Greek cheese (4)
9 Deity (8)
10 Ski run (5)
11 Noisy confusion (7)
14 Alone (13)
16 Release from captivity (3,4)
18 Shoot with great precision (5)
20 Out of date (8)
22 Cut of meat (4)
23 Large pebbles (6)
24 Begrudge (6)

Down

2 Compliance (9)
3 Flexible (7)
4 Periodic movement of the sea (4)
5 Wrapper for a letter (8)
6 Leases (5)
7 Small shelter (3)
12 Immunity (9)
13 Without a fixed abode (8)
15 Render utterly perplexed (7)
17 Scowl (5)
19 Put on an item of clothing (4)
21 Mainly nocturnal mammal (3)

Across

1 Consumes food (4)

3 Green vegetable (8)

9 Remedy for everything (7)

10 Observed (5)

11 Mother-of-pearl (5)

12 Graceful in form (7)

13 One of the halogens (6)

15 Part of a motor (6)

17 Made certain of (7)

18 Excuse of any kind (5)

20 Show triumphant joy (5)

21 Japanese flower arranging (7)

22 Fortified wines (8)

23 Overly curious (4)

Down

1 Ebullience (13)

2 Cloak (5)

4 Raised (6)

5 Intense (12)

6 Social reject (7)

7 Vagueness (13)

8 Creator of film scripts (12)

14 Quarrel (7)

16 Tips and instruction (6)

19 State of the USA (5)

Across

1 Remains of something damaged (8)
5 Island of Indonesia (4)
8 Musical toy (5)
9 Piece of furniture (7)
10 Impose one's will (7)
12 Highest mountain (7)
14 Adding together (7)
16 Brushed off the face (of hair) (7)
18 Animal fat (7)
19 Confound (5)
20 Relax and do little (4)
21 Laughed (8)

Down

1 Rouse from sleep (4)
2 Biochemical catalyst (6)
3 General erudition (9)
4 Ingenious device (6)
6 Soak up (6)
7 Concurring (8)
11 Very predictable (9)
12 Hamper (8)
13 Topics for debate (6)
14 Complex carbohydrate (6)
15 Country in the Middle East (6)
17 Curve in a road (4)

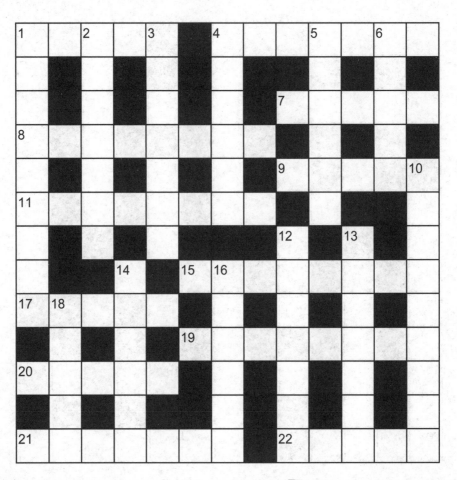

Across

1 Beasts of burden (5)

4 Rod used in weightlifting (7)

7 Penitent (5)

8 Rushing (2,1,5)

9 Assumed appearance (5)

11 Unseemly (8)

15 Where photographs are developed (8)

17 Propels the body through water (5)

19 European country (8)

20 Seabirds (5)

21 Made a garment by intertwining threads (7)

22 Devout (5)

Down

1 Drugs used to treat diseases (9)

2 Molecules that bind to others (7)

3 Squeeze into a compact mass (7)

4 Unproductive (of land) (6)

5 Shoe (6)

6 Lingers furtively (5)

10 The origin of a word (9)

12 Moving on ice (7)

13 Expelled air abruptly (7)

14 Deposit knowledge (6)

16 Approximately (6)

18 Rouse from sleep (5)

Across

1 Tone down (4)
3 Approximate (8)
9 Strange or mysterious (7)
10 Lock of hair (5)
11 Version of the blues (6-6)
14 North American nation (abbrev.) (3)
16 Visual representation (5)
17 Positive answer (3)
18 Highly abstract (12)
21 One of the United Arab Emirates (5)
22 One absorbed in themselves (7)
23 Permits to do something (8)
24 Cobras (4)

Down

1 Sign of approval (6-2)
2 Piece of code to automate a task (5)
4 Timid (3)
5 Shyness (12)
6 Useful feature of a place (7)
7 The Orient (4)
8 Total destruction (12)
12 Ire (5)
13 Makes remote; cuts off (8)
15 Sour in taste (7)
19 Babies' beds (5)
20 Effigy (4)
22 Make a living with difficulty (3)

CROSSWORD 339

Across

7 Stocky (8)
8 Uncle's wife (4)
9 Sixty minutes (4)
10 Not necessary (8)
11 Need (7)
12 Cleans (5)
15 Fighter (5)
17 Bison (7)
20 Bathing costume (8)
22 Smack with the hand (4)
23 Ship's complement (4)
24 Experienced pain (8)

Down

1 Officially cancel (6)
2 Orchestral piece at the beginning of an opera (8)
3 Title appended to a man's name (7)
4 Stench (5)
5 Body of water (4)
6 Make something new (6)
13 Undo; loosen (8)
14 Show to be reasonable (7)
16 Ahead (6)
18 Ordeal (anag.) (6)
19 Subdue (5)
21 Cuts the grass (4)

Across

1 Title used for a French woman (6)
4 Of practical benefit (6)
9 Less heavy (7)
10 Mutters (7)
11 Wards (anag.) (5)
12 Titles (5)
14 Goes through carefully (5)
15 Chocolate powder (5)
17 Small group ruling a country (5)
18 Tuneful (7)
20 Foes (7)
21 Bank employee (6)
22 Evaluate (6)

Down

1 Disease of the body (6)
2 Opinionated and inflexible (8)
3 Nocturnal insects (5)
5 Homilies (7)
6 Opposite of pass (4)
7 Glasses contain these (6)
8 The military (5,6)
13 During the intervening period (8)
14 Young pilchard (7)
15 Building material (6)
16 Temporary failures of concentration (6)
17 Sturdy motor vehicles (5)
19 Quieten down; send to sleep (4)

CROSSWORD 341

Across

1 Half of six (5)
4 Extraordinary occurrence (7)
7 Hits swiftly (5)
8 Indistinct; hazy (8)
9 Making a knot in (5)
11 Women noted for great courage (8)
15 Extremely lovable (8)
17 Delay or linger (5)
19 Merry-go-round (8)
20 Precious gem (5)
21 Selfishness (7)
22 Iffy (5)

Down

1 Cutting; incisive (9)
2 Act of stealing (7)
3 Notable feat (7)
4 Sixty seconds (6)
5 Continuously (6)
6 Language of the Romans (5)
10 Study of ancestry (9)
12 Not straight (7)
13 Embarrassed (7)
14 Imagined whilst asleep (6)
16 Single-celled alga (6)
18 With a forward motion (5)

Across

1 South Asian garment (4)

3 Amazes (8)

9 Important dietary component (7)

10 Speed music is played at (5)

11 Senseless (5)

12 Beg (7)

13 Units of heat (6)

15 Person to whom a lease is granted (6)

17 Seed with a fibrous husk and edible white flesh (7)

18 Faint bird cry (5)

20 Pulsate (5)

21 First in importance (7)

22 Acted with hesitation (8)

23 Give temporarily (4)

Down

1 Worldly-wise (13)

2 Dry red wine (5)

4 Transmitter (6)

5 Fully extended (12)

6 Fourth book of the Bible (7)

7 Easily angered (5-8)

8 Resolvable (12)

14 Extract (7)

16 Level plain without trees (6)

19 Expulsion (5)

CROSSWORD 343

Across

1 Highly excited (4)
3 Relinquish a throne (8)
9 Readying (7)
10 Finely cut straw (5)
11 Fix the result in advance (3)
12 Lowest point (5)
13 Songbirds (5)
15 Inner circle (5)
17 Shallow recess (5)
18 Monstrous humanoid creature (3)
19 Run away with a lover (5)
20 Gold or silver in bulk (7)
21 Written agreements (8)
22 Release (4)

Down

1 Distribution (13)
2 Outstanding (of a debt) (5)
4 Larger (6)
5 Heartbroken (12)
6 Gave a prize (7)
7 Fizz (13)
8 Action of moving a thing from its position (12)
14 Type of sugar (7)
16 Pocket of air in a sphere of liquid (6)
18 Willow twig (5)

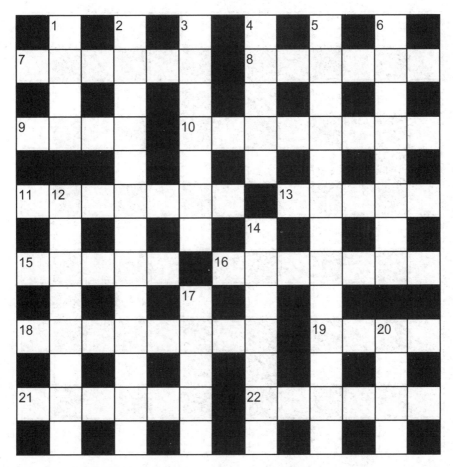

Across

7 Long mountain chain (6)

8 Removed the skin (6)

9 Obtains (4)

10 Alloy of copper and tin (8)

11 Irritable (7)

13 Linear measure units; limes (anag.) (5)

15 Removes water from a boat (5)

16 Deviate from the subject at hand (7)

18 Answer to a problem (8)

19 Pulls at (4)

21 Look out (6)

22 Consisting of flowers (6)

Down

1 Soaring bird of prey (4)

2 Dealing with different societies (5-8)

3 Chiefly (7)

4 Slap with an open hand (5)

5 Process of worsening (13)

6 Disputants (8)

12 Argued logically (8)

14 Stand for (7)

17 Blends (5)

20 Hardy ruminant mammal (4)

Across

1 Crashes into (8)
5 Thaw (anag.) (4)
9 Russian spirit (5)
10 Heavily loaded (5)
11 Personification (10)
14 Least young (6)
15 Turmoil (6)
17 Not moving (10)
20 Genuflect (5)
21 Religious table (5)
22 Short letter (4)
23 Segment of the spinal column (8)

Down

1 Bay (4)
2 Removable covers (4)
3 Not allowable (12)
4 Newspaper boss (6)
6 Mammal with a spiny coat (8)
7 Medicine (8)
8 Crucial (3,9)
12 Abandoned (8)
13 Adjoining (8)
16 Ask a person to come (6)
18 Remnant (4)
19 Killer whale (4)

Across

1 Small shoots (6)
5 Slander (6)
8 Walk awkwardly (4)
9 Definitions (8)
10 Induce fear (5)
11 Public speakers (7)
14 Relevance (13)
16 High spirits (7)
18 Sweeping implement (5)
20 Film with an exciting plot (8)
22 Upper part of the body (4)
23 Confirmed a decision (6)
24 Money available to be spent (6)

Down

2 Foremost; main (9)
3 Endanger (7)
4 Identical (4)
5 Verbal attack (8)
6 Behave amorously (5)
7 Periodic publication (abbrev.) (3)
12 Explanation (9)
13 Educated (8)
15 Staggered (7)
17 Social division in some societies (5)
19 Thrash (4)
21 Leap on one foot (3)

CROSSWORD 347

Across

1 Excavates (4)
3 Feud (8)
9 Expressed disapproval facially (7)
10 Supply sparingly; sandpiper (5)
11 Armature of a generator (5)
12 Impresario (7)
13 Labelling (6)
15 Women who are about to marry (6)
17 Distributing (7)
18 Feeling of boredom (5)
20 Money (5)
21 Escaping (7)
22 Christmas season (8)
23 Openly refuse to obey an order (4)

Down

1 In a servile manner (13)
2 Thin mortar (5)
4 Of the greatest age (6)
5 Ill-mannered (12)
6 Pared (7)
7 Amazingly (13)
8 Inflexible (12)
14 Melodious (7)
16 Accepted (6)
19 Sound of any kind (5)

Across

1 Portray (6)
4 Cause resentment (6)
9 Perform magic tricks (7)
10 Military gestures (7)
11 Unshapely masses; swellings (5)
12 Craftily (5)
14 Snag; minor problem (5)
15 Stagnant (5)
17 Aromatic resin (5)
18 Japanese warrior (7)
20 One's mental attitude (7)
21 Layers (anag.) (6)
22 Slows down (6)

Down

1 Easily handled (6)
2 Region of a shadow (8)
3 Bludgeons (5)
5 Daft (7)
6 Give out (4)
7 Showy (6)
8 Poverty (11)
13 Annual (8)
14 Gossip (7)
15 Female sibling (6)
16 Trembles (6)
17 Usage measuring device (5)
19 Letters and parcels generally (4)

CROSSWORD 349

Across

1 Cereal grains used as food (4)
3 Cogitating (8)
9 Cruel use of authority (7)
10 Desires (5)
11 Large Brazilian city (3,2,7)
13 Far away from home (6)
15 Workroom of a painter (6)
17 Graphical (12)
20 Ascend (5)
21 Protective layers (7)
22 Our galaxy (5,3)
23 Average value (4)

Down

1 Sudden eruption (8)
2 Trunk of the body (5)
4 Period of prosperity (6)
5 Second part of the Bible (3,9)
6 Blanked (7)
7 Take a breath owing to astonishment (4)
8 Understandably (12)
12 Soft leather shoe (8)
14 Existing at the beginning (7)
16 Flowering plant (6)
18 Stretched tight (of a muscle) (5)
19 Con; swindle (4)

CROSSWORD 350

Across

1 Lowered one's body (8)
5 Concern; worry (4)
8 Saying (5)
9 Mundane (7)
10 Harmonious relationship (7)
12 Small bone (7)
14 Variety of rummy (7)
16 Diplomatic building (7)
18 Experienced serviceman (7)
19 Arrive at (5)
20 Part of a pedestal (4)
21 Experiencing great hunger (8)

Down

1 Crustacean (4)
2 Speaks publicly (6)
3 E.g. ammonia and caustic soda (9)
4 Extensive domain (6)
6 River in South America (6)
7 And so on (2,6)
11 Robber (9)
12 Perceived (8)
13 Became less intense (6)
14 Young swan (6)
15 Sightseeing trip in Africa (6)
17 Dull car sound (4)

CROSSWORD 351

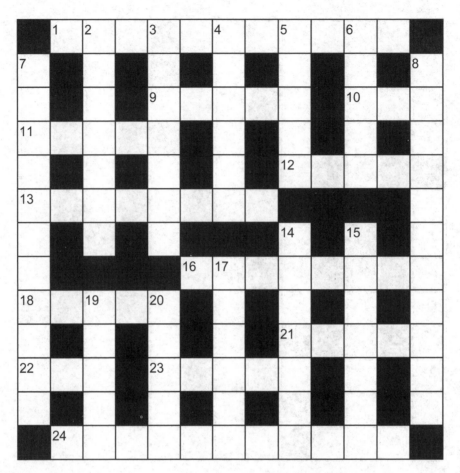

Across

1 Domineering (11)
9 Variety of coffee (5)
10 Hair style (3)
11 Mark of repetition (5)
12 Type of leather (5)
13 Wood preserver (8)
16 Brilliant musical performers (8)
18 Reversed (5)
21 Ironic metaphor (5)
22 Made-up statement (3)
23 Baking appliances (5)
24 Rude (11)

Down

2 Wine merchant (7)
3 Regret (7)
4 Bodyguard (6)
5 Large quantities of paper (5)
6 Admirable (5)
7 Boldly (11)
8 Compulsively (11)
14 Cowboy hat (7)
15 Ancient wise king (7)
17 Arthropod (6)
19 You usually do this whilst asleep (5)
20 Steered a car (5)

Across

1 Roll of parchment (6)
5 Give formal consent to (6)
8 Joke (4)
9 The training of birds of prey (8)
10 Exclusive story (5)
11 Period of conflict (7)
14 In a disbelieving manner (13)
16 Pay homage to (7)
18 Mexican tortilla wraps (5)
20 Fortify against attack (8)
22 Beloved; expensive (4)
23 Lived by (6)
24 Book of accounts (6)

Down

2 Gradual increase in loudness (9)
3 Located in the fresh air (7)
4 Raise up (4)
5 Dependable (8)
6 Game fish (5)
7 Soft animal hair (3)
12 Improve (9)
13 Physiologically dependent (8)
15 Single-handed (7)
17 Piece of broken pottery (5)
19 Repast (4)
21 Gang (3)

CROSSWORD 353

Across

7 Prance around (6)
8 Language (6)
9 Action word (4)
10 Silliness (8)
11 Orbs (7)
13 Financial resources (5)
15 Rivulet (5)
16 Copy (7)
18 Heavy rain (8)
19 Respiratory organ of fish (4)
21 Driers (anag.) (6)
22 E.g. a dog (6)

Down

1 Sweet dessert (4)
2 Having unusually flexible joints (6-7)
3 Examines in detail (7)
4 Rigid (5)
5 Not clever (13)
6 Slower than sound (8)
12 Recurring at intervals (8)
14 Furtiveness (7)
17 Timber beam (5)
20 Fabric used to dress wounds (4)

Across

1 High-pitched flute (4)
3 Act of leaving out (8)
9 Make more entertaining (7)
10 Coming after (5)
11 Directions (12)
13 Small pit or cavity (6)
15 Greek goddess of wisdom (6)
17 Intolerable (12)
20 In the company of (5)
21 See (7)
22 Atmospheric moisture (8)
23 Final (4)

Down

1 Bendy (8)
2 Drops to the ground (5)
4 Threaten (6)
5 Narcissism (4-8)
6 Ardent (7)
7 Standard regarded as typical (4)
8 Ate too much (12)
12 Footpath for pedestrians (8)
14 Comply (with rules) (7)
16 Not sinking (6)
18 Former name of Myanmar (5)
19 Uproarious party (4)

CROSSWORD 355

Across

1 Of considerable size (11)
9 Cool down (5)
10 Metal container; is able to (3)
11 Search thoroughly for (5)
12 Elevated step (5)
13 Quality of being holy (8)
16 Confine (8)
18 Domesticated (5)
21 Speak without preparation (2-3)
22 Plaything (3)
23 Short choral composition (5)
24 Perplexing situation (11)

Down

2 Reversing something (7)
3 Place out of sight (7)
4 Get off (6)
5 Leans at an angle (5)
6 Capital of Ghana (5)
7 Revive (11)
8 Stubborn (11)
14 Layer or band of rock (7)
15 One thousand million (7)
17 Excitingly strange (6)
19 District council head (5)
20 Vaulted (5)

Across

7 Concise (8)

8 Lie in ambush (4)

9 Create (4)

10 Water (8)

11 Made a guttural sound (7)

12 Assembly rooms (5)

15 Father (5)

17 Puzzles composed of many pieces (7)

20 Rank or status (8)

22 True and actual (4)

23 Cut down a tree (4)

24 Solitary (8)

Down

1 Domestic assistant (2,4)

2 Showed a TV show (8)

3 Inner parts of things (7)

4 Work of fiction (5)

5 Standard (4)

6 Savage (6)

13 Obscure (8)

14 Fixing; manipulating (7)

16 Deer horn (6)

18 Devastating blow (6)

19 Clock faces (5)

21 The world's longest river (4)

CROSSWORD 357

Across

1 In the open air (8)
5 Edible fat (4)
8 Our planet (5)
9 Identifying outfit (7)
10 Window furnishing (7)
12 Thoroughly (2,5)
14 Small explosive bomb (7)
16 Early childhood (7)
18 Coolness (7)
19 Bony structure in the head (5)
20 Precious stones (4)
21 Sniffing at (8)

Down

1 Once more (4)
2 Did agricultural work (6)
3 E.g. a resident of Addis Ababa (9)
4 Clasp (6)
6 Without ethics (6)
7 Have power over (8)
11 Practice session for a performance (9)
12 Provoking (8)
13 State publicly (6)
14 Mineral used to make plaster of Paris (6)
15 Long-legged rodent (6)
17 Golf (anag.) (4)

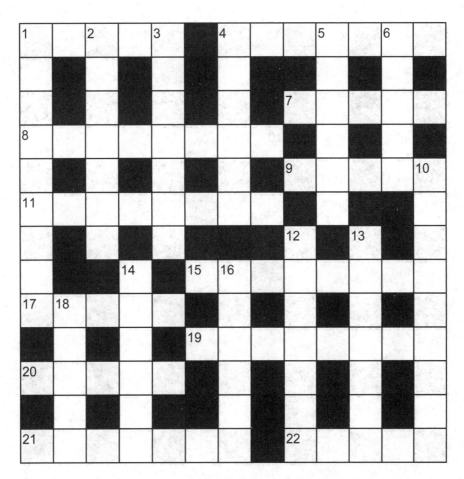

Across

1 Tell off (5)

4 Item of clothing (7)

7 Issue forth with force (5)

8 Usually (8)

9 E.g. taste or touch (5)

11 Least heavy (8)

15 Put at risk (8)

17 Hits hard (5)

19 Food poisoning (8)

20 Descend rapidly (5)

21 Repository (7)

22 Unfortunately (5)

Down

1 Silent (9)

2 Surplus or excess (7)

3 Line of rulers (7)

4 Interrogates (6)

5 Sample (anag.) (6)

6 Words that identify things (5)

10 Exceedingly (9)

12 Becomes fully grown (7)

13 Caused to burn (7)

14 Caress and kiss (6)

16 Pasta strip (6)

18 Less high (5)

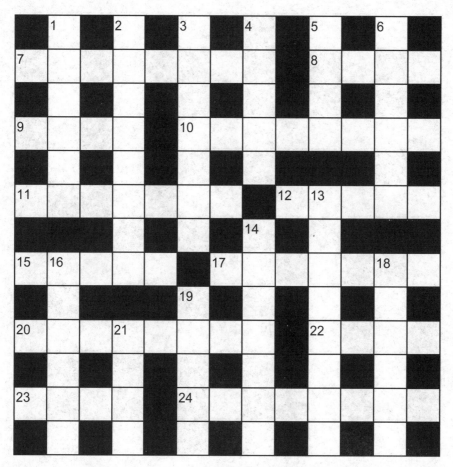

Across

7 Person who gives a sermon (8)

8 Feeble (of an excuse) (4)

9 Anxiety; dread (4)

10 Adversary (8)

11 Written law (7)

12 Hurts (5)

15 Neck warmer (5)

17 Artificial barrier in a watercourse (7)

20 Catch a conversation between others (8)

22 Centre of a sail (4)

23 Worry about (4)

24 Water-resistant jacket (8)

Down

1 Imperative (6)

2 One who tells a story (8)

3 Husky (7)

4 Vault under a church (5)

5 Large family (4)

6 US rapper (6)

13 Vigorous exercises (8)

14 Sheikdom in the Persian Gulf (7)

16 Grotto (6)

18 Cordial (6)

19 Sorrowful (5)

21 Rank (4)

Across

1 Dulls (4)

3 Red fruits eaten as vegetables (8)

9 Alternative form (7)

10 Operate a motor vehicle (5)

11 Careful consideration (12)

13 Loops with running knots (6)

15 Excessively ornate (of literature) (6)

17 Physics of movement through air (12)

20 Gemstones (5)

21 Large web-footed bird (7)

22 Grow in a vigorous way (8)

23 Computer memory unit (4)

Down

1 Money paid to shareholders (8)

2 Ethical (5)

4 Semiaquatic fish-eating mammals (6)

5 And also (12)

6 River in South America (7)

7 Perceives (4)

8 Troublemaker (6-6)

12 Gibberish (8)

14 Aromatic herb (7)

16 Insect larvae (6)

18 Needing to be scratched (5)

19 Predatory canine mammal (4)

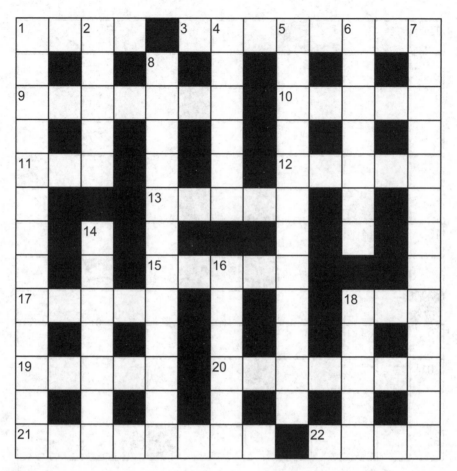

Across

1 Not hard (4)
3 Frozen dessert (3,5)
9 Approximately (7)
10 Sends out in the post (5)
11 Opposite of bottom (3)
12 Period of time in history (5)
13 Church instrument (5)
15 Display freely (5)
17 Sing softly (5)
18 Sound of a cow (3)
19 Beer (5)
20 Deals with (7)
21 Longing (8)
22 Ancient city (4)

Down

1 Tactically (13)
2 Fall heavily (5)
4 Weeping (6)
5 Beginning (12)
6 One event in a sequence (7)
7 Naughtily (13)
8 Evergreen shrub (12)
14 State of the USA (7)
16 Poorly dressed child (6)
18 Type of tooth (5)

Across

1 Use these to row a boat (4)

3 Light axe (8)

9 Virtuoso solo passage (7)

10 Question (5)

11 State of the USA (12)

13 Type of rain cloud (6)

15 Make beloved (6)

17 Prediction or expectation (12)

20 Not telling the truth (5)

21 Polygon having ten sides (7)

22 Irritating (8)

23 Cook slowly in liquid (4)

Down

1 Resident (8)

2 Noble gas (5)

4 Prophet (6)

5 Person one knows (12)

6 Simian (7)

7 Implements used to unlock doors (4)

8 Modestly (12)

12 Pristine (5-3)

14 Stately residence (7)

16 Concealed from view (6)

18 Gold block (5)

19 Primitive plant (4)

CROSSWORD 363

Across

1 Merger (11)
9 Angry dispute (3-2)
10 Very cold (3)
11 Directly opposite in character (5)
12 Crawl (5)
13 Tepid (8)
16 Neck injury (8)
18 Spring flower (5)
21 Steer (anag.) (5)
22 Clumsy person (3)
23 Paved area (5)
24 Act of publishing in several places (11)

Down

2 Reticular (7)
3 Narrow trenches (7)
4 Bit of partly burnt wood (6)
5 Invigorating medicine (5)
6 Expect; think that (5)
7 Name or title (11)
8 Compassionate (11)
14 Candid (7)
15 A very skilled performer (7)
17 Manic (6)
19 Towering (5)
20 Supplied by tube (5)

CROSSWORD 364

Across

1 Bird beak (4)
3 Expanded (8)
9 Pamphlet (7)
10 Endures (5)
11 Room attached to a house (12)
14 Feline (3)
16 Lazy person; layabout (5)
17 22nd Greek letter (3)
18 Not on purpose; inadvertently (12)
21 Longest river in Europe (5)
22 Decorative altar cloth (7)
23 Blushed (8)
24 Therefore (4)

Down

1 Device that regulates water flow (8)
2 Find out (5)
4 Item for catching fish (3)
5 Repetition of the same sound (12)
6 Of the stomach (7)
7 Quantity of medication (4)
8 Unlawful (12)
12 Regard highly (5)
13 Two-wheeled vehicles (8)
15 Excited agreeably (7)
19 Gate fastener (5)
20 Affirm with confidence (4)
22 Enemy (3)

CROSSWORD 365

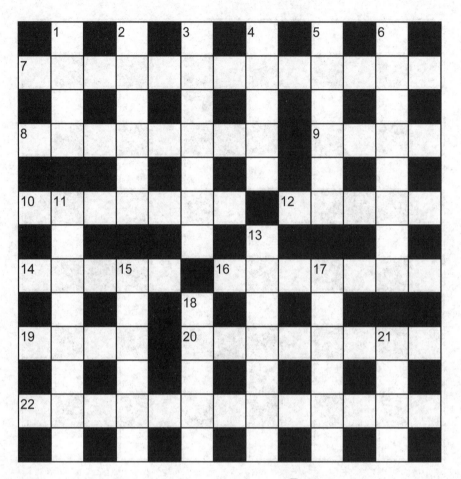

Across

7 Rude (13)

8 Opposite of eastward (8)

9 Urge on (4)

10 Portable enclosure for infants (7)

12 Destined (5)

14 Breaks in two (5)

16 Rest days (7)

19 Wagers (4)

20 Certain to fail (8)

22 Official recognition (13)

Down

1 Eat at a restaurant (4)

2 Showing courage (6)

3 Feeling guilty (7)

4 Leashes (5)

5 Mark of disgrace (6)

6 Done in a kindly manner; sympathetically (8)

11 Clemency (8)

13 Movable models of people (7)

15 Show-offs (6)

17 Widen (6)

18 Outbuildings (5)

21 Black powdery substance (4)

Across

1 Mature person (5)
4 Walk unsteadily (7)
7 Courageous (5)
8 Inventive; creative (8)
9 Small imaginary being (5)
11 Drink consumed before bed (8)
15 Aggressor (8)
17 Triangular wall part (5)
19 Squid dish (8)
20 Sharp end (5)
21 Speak to (7)
22 Oozes (5)

Down

1 Bordering (9)
2 Throw into disorder (7)
3 Computer keyboard users (7)
4 Huge desert in North Africa (6)
5 Subject to death (6)
6 Lobed glandular organ (5)
10 Young racehorses (9)
12 Yellow fruits (7)
13 Country whose capital is Kiev (7)
14 Flat; two-dimensional (6)
16 Expresses gratitude (6)
18 Preclude (5)

CROSSWORD 367

Across
1 Annoy (4)
3 Building material (8)
9 Stimulated; urged on (7)
10 African country whose capital is Niamey (5)
11 Impossible to achieve (12)
13 Dirty; grimy (6)
15 Flowering plant with a prickly stem (6)
17 Duplication (12)
20 Broadcast again (5)
21 Wound covering (7)
22 E.g. Usain Bolt and Mo Farah (8)
23 Seat (anag.) (4)

Down
1 Be wrong about (8)
2 Animal life of a region (5)
4 Establish by law (6)
5 Recovering from illness (of a person) (12)
6 Envelops (7)
7 Monetary unit of Spain (4)
8 Bump (12)
12 Makes defamatory remarks (8)
14 Dig out of the ground (7)
16 Fit for consumption (6)
18 Angry (5)
19 Song for a solo voice (4)

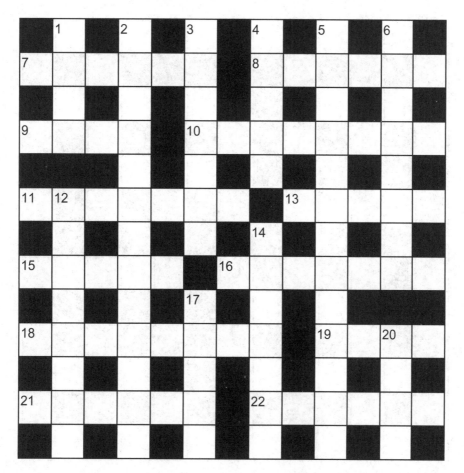

Across

7 Remove weapons (6)

8 Loudspeaker (6)

9 Retained (4)

10 One with another (8)

11 Attains (7)

13 Model figures used as toys (5)

15 Overly sentimental (5)

16 Pals (7)

18 Flatter (6,2)

19 Shelf at the foot of a window opening (4)

21 Urge to do something (6)

22 Unkempt (of hair) (6)

Down

1 Find pleasant (4)

2 Involvement (13)

3 Crazy about someone (7)

4 Small branches (5)

5 Contentious (13)

6 Drove back (8)

12 Fluent in the use of language (8)

14 Suggest (7)

17 Smiles broadly (5)

20 Official records (4)

CROSSWORD 369

Across

1 Tip (8)
5 Ward (anag.) (4)
8 Type of coffee drink (5)
9 Generally; in summary (7)
10 Admittedly (7)
12 Fastest animal on land (7)
14 In the fresh air (7)
16 Angered (7)
18 Japanese dish of raw fish (7)
19 Bore into (5)
20 Flows (4)
21 Regularity of nature (8)

Down

1 Common seabird (4)
2 Clothing (6)
3 Unnatural (9)
4 Natural depression (6)
6 Cooks in the oven (6)
7 Thoroughly cooked (of meat) (4-4)
11 Capital of the Netherlands (9)
12 Skin care product (8)
13 Agreement or concord (6)
14 Strange thing (6)
15 Charge with a crime (6)
17 Participate in a game (4)

Across

7 More slothful (6)

8 Musical dramas (6)

9 US monetary unit (4)

10 Reserved in advance (3-5)

11 Enumerated (7)

13 Fret (5)

15 Below zero (of temperature) (5)

16 Tribune (anag.) (7)

18 Cutlery used to stir a drink (8)

19 Mocks (4)

21 Soundless (6)

22 Rubs (6)

Down

1 Possess (4)

2 Successful and eminent (13)

3 Clad (7)

4 Shoes (5)

5 Animal used for heavy work (5,2,6)

6 Chinese language (8)

12 Common salad dressing (5,3)

14 Supply; provide (7)

17 Puts in order (5)

20 Sharp cry of a dog (4)

CROSSWORD 371

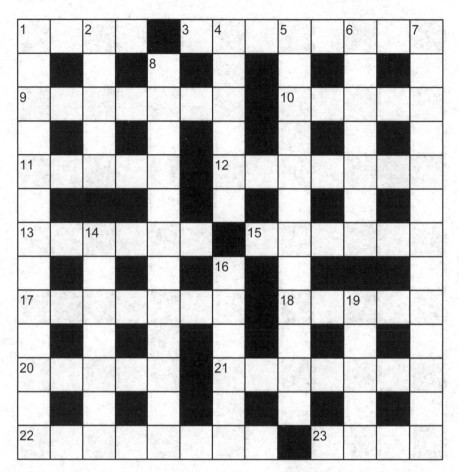

Across

1 Soothe (4)
3 Announce publicly (8)
9 Repositories of antiques (7)
10 Start of (5)
11 Land measures (5)
12 Breastbone (7)
13 Deduces from evidence (6)
15 Long and very narrow (6)
17 Ardently; keenly (7)
18 Upper part of the leg (5)
20 Dark wood (5)
21 Works in an amateurish way (7)
22 Prison term (8)
23 Woes; problems (4)

Down

1 Militant aggressiveness (13)
2 Roles (anag.) (5)
4 Oppose (6)
5 Tight (of clothing) (5-7)
6 Lack of (7)
7 Process of transformation (of an insect) (13)
8 Short tale told to children (7,5)
14 Warning device for ships (7)
16 Believer in the occult (6)
19 Model; perfect (5)

CROSSWORD 372

Across

1 Not pleasing to listen to (8)
5 James Bond film (2,2)
9 Space (anag.) (5)
10 Parts of eggs (5)
11 Unable to talk (10)
14 Explanation (6)
15 Sheepskin (6)
17 Domesticated cavies (6,4)
20 Bird sound; chirp (5)
21 Bring about (5)
22 Corrode (4)
23 Course of study (8)

Down

1 Thoughtfulness (4)
2 Short sleeps (4)
3 Repository for misplaced items (4,8)
4 Drenched (6)
6 Assuages (8)
7 Thinks about something continually (8)
8 Based on legend (12)
12 Less dark (8)
13 Sloth (8)
16 Frankly (6)
18 Incandescent lamp (4)
19 Belonging to a woman (4)

CROSSWORD 373

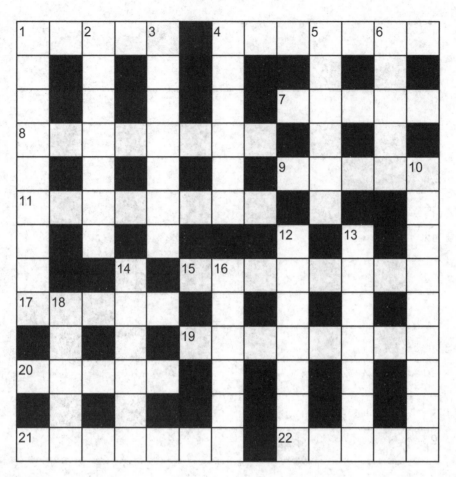

Across

1 Stories (5)
4 Drowses (anag.) (7)
7 Obtains something desirable (5)
8 Destined to fail (3-5)
9 Fed up (5)
11 Complete (8)
15 Sleep disorder (8)
17 Sailing vessel (5)
19 Reference point; norm (8)
20 Receded (5)
21 Funny (7)
22 Show indifference with the shoulders (5)

Down

1 Normally; usually (9)
2 Anarchic (7)
3 Gusty winds (7)
4 Discover (6)
5 Type of ski race (6)
6 Extent or limit (5)
10 Difficult to do (9)
12 Demureness (7)
13 Item used by asthma sufferers (7)
14 Steering devices (6)
16 Spice (6)
18 Collection of songs (5)

Across

1 Developed into (6)
4 Not rough (6)
9 Not spiritual or sacred (7)
10 Swears (7)
11 Large indefinite quantities (5)
12 Upper limits (5)
14 Fiercely (5)
15 Gave out light (5)
17 Hit with the fist (5)
18 Unite together (7)
20 Place in order (7)
21 Capital of Bahrain (6)
22 Treatises (6)

Down

1 Common volcanic rock (6)
2 White crested parrot (8)
3 Men (5)
5 Baffling puzzle (7)
6 Noes (anag.) (4)
7 Makes a sibilant sound (6)
8 Conventional (11)
13 Beginnings (8)
14 Great courage (7)
15 Triangular bone (6)
16 Leaders (6)
17 Roofed entrance to a house (5)
19 Noble gas (4)

CROSSWORD 375

Across

1 Attack with severe criticism (6)
5 19th Greek letter (3)
7 Redden (5)
8 A dancer or singer (7)
9 More delicate (5)
10 Thing that is easily done (8)
12 Reach a specified level (6)
14 Cloud type (6)
17 Extremely happy (8)
18 Thin roofing slabs (5)
20 Painter (anag.) (7)
21 Strike (5)
22 Word expressing negation (3)
23 Emotionally dependent (6)

Down

2 Lap of a track (7)
3 Belonging to the past (8)
4 Fit of petty annoyance (4)
5 Narrower (7)
6 Remove clothes (7)
7 Outdoor fundraising events (5)
11 On the shore of a sea (8)
12 Public sale with bidders (7)
13 Greatest in height (7)
15 Combining (7)
16 Long flower-stalk (5)
19 Propel the body through water (4)

Across

1 Unfortunate (11)
9 Opposite of old (5)
10 Snip (3)
11 Stadium (5)
12 Pertaining to the sun (5)
13 Scope for freedom (8)
16 Come before in time (8)
18 Ungainly (5)
21 Move on hands and knees (5)
22 E.g. pecan (3)
23 Dance club (5)
24 Type of fat (11)

Down

2 Anticipates (7)
3 E.g. kings and queens (7)
4 Routed (anag.) (6)
5 The protection of a particular person (5)
6 In the area (5)
7 Questioning a statement (11)
8 Narrator (11)
14 Greet (7)
15 In reality; actually (2,5)
17 Hospital carers (6)
19 Sorceress (5)
20 Mountain cry (5)

CROSSWORD 377

Across

1 Wine container (4)
3 Country in North East Africa (8)
9 Summary of results (7)
10 Make a map of (5)
11 Cutting tool (3)
12 Musical note (5)
13 Brace (5)
15 Repository (5)
17 Divide by two (5)
18 Intentionally so written (3)
19 Intended (5)
20 Mournful (7)
21 Heath (8)
22 Type of high-energy radiation (1-3)

Down

1 Plant with bright flowers (13)
2 Strong fibrous tissue (5)
4 Frozen plain (6)
5 Contradictory (12)
6 Clearly (7)
7 In a reflex manner (13)
8 Occurring at the same time (12)
14 Vent for molten lava (7)
16 Forgive (6)
18 More secure (5)

Across

1 Sapper (anag.) (6)
7 Full of twists and turns (8)
8 Helpful hint (3)
9 Keep watch over an area (6)
10 Skirt worn by ballerinas (4)
11 Hear a court case anew (5)
13 Worked dough (7)
15 Refrain from (7)
17 Short notes (5)
21 Singe (4)
22 Left (6)
23 Goal (3)
24 Holding on tightly (8)
25 Device that detects a physical
   property (6)

Down

1 Golf club (6)
2 Marionette (6)
3 Grim (5)
4 Country whose capital is
   Dublin (7)
5 Luggage item (8)
6 Steal livestock (6)
12 Shy; bashful (8)
14 Caused by motion (7)
16 See or observe (6)
18 Military decorations (6)
19 Season (6)
20 E.g. performs karaoke (5)

CROSSWORD 379

Across

1 Official language of Pakistan (4)
3 Sheath for a sword (8)
9 Capricious; skittish (7)
10 Exposes secret information (5)
11 Edge of a cup (3)
12 Gamble (5)
13 Upright (5)
15 Look at fixedly (5)
17 Remnant of a dying fire (5)
18 Hip (anag.) (3)
19 Small airship (5)
20 Unsurpassed (3-4)
21 Commonplace (8)
22 Circular movement of water (4)

Down

1 Incapable of being anticipated (13)
2 Belief in a god or gods (5)
4 Wolflike wild dog (6)
5 Disregarding the rules (5,3,4)
6 Mercury alloy (7)
7 Devastatingly (13)
8 Art of planning a dance (12)
14 Awe-inspiring (7)
16 Domesticated llama (6)
18 Examined furtively (5)

Across

1 Tall vases (4)
3 Walks unsteadily (8)
9 Complicated (7)
10 Indian lute (5)
11 Doctor (5)
12 Planet (7)
13 Opposite of winners (6)
15 Woodland (6)
17 Sudden inclination to act (7)
18 Unabridged (5)
20 Images of deities (5)
21 Quivering singing effect (7)
22 Estimating (8)
23 Seek (anag.) (4)

Down

1 Stoical; patient (13)
2 Wanderer (5)
4 Difficult (6)
5 Made in bulk (4-8)
6 Salad vegetable (7)
7 Clandestine (13)
8 Decomposition by a current (12)
14 Assume (7)
16 Make tidier (6)
19 Device used to tell the time (5)

CROSSWORD 381

Across

1 Hostages (8)
5 A swamp grass (4)
9 Put an idea in someone's mind (5)
10 Stand up (5)
11 Feigning (10)
14 16 of these in a pound (6)
15 Bleach (6)
17 Below the level of consciousness (10)
20 Thing that imparts motion (5)
21 Hard and durable (5)
22 Clarets (4)
23 Beetle larva that bores into timber (8)

Down

1 Manage (4)
2 Mountain top (4)
3 Middleman (12)
4 Removes from one's property (6)
6 Begin (8)
7 Coming out of (8)
8 Lacking courage (5-7)
12 User; purchaser (8)
13 With undiminished force (8)
16 Emperor of Japan (6)
18 Greek spirit (4)
19 Fraud (4)

Across

1 Frank (6)
5 What a spider weaves (3)
7 Partly melted snow (5)
8 Move slowly (7)
9 Broom (5)
10 Resolute; obstinate (8)
12 Small whirlpools (6)
14 Seek out (6)
17 Of striking beauty (8)
18 Boasts about (5)
20 Illuminate (5,2)
21 Garment with sleeves (5)
22 Not bright; darken (3)
23 E.g. grapes and bananas (6)

Down

2 Introduced air to (7)
3 Owing money (8)
4 Deprived of sensation (4)
5 Speak very quietly (7)
6 Flaw (7)
7 Prophets (5)
11 Adolescent (8)
12 Helped to happen (7)
13 Early 20th century art movement (7)
15 Direct an orchestra (7)
16 Avocet-like wader (5)
19 Drink greedily (4)

CROSSWORD 383

Across

7 Form the base for (8)
8 Related by blood (4)
9 Tense (4)
10 Making law (8)
11 Steadfast (7)
12 Protective covering (5)
15 Social gathering (5)
17 Inert gaseous element (7)
20 Disdainful rejection (5-3)
22 Sound of a pig (4)
23 Repeated jazz phrase (4)
24 Versions of a book (8)

Down

1 Whole (6)
2 Cause deliberate damage to (8)
3 Ability to speak another language very well (7)
4 Houston's state (5)
5 A flat float (4)
6 Intend (anag.) (6)
13 Mesmerism (8)
14 Fabled monster (7)
16 Scared (6)
18 Possessing (6)
19 Bent; bandy (5)
21 Strain (4)

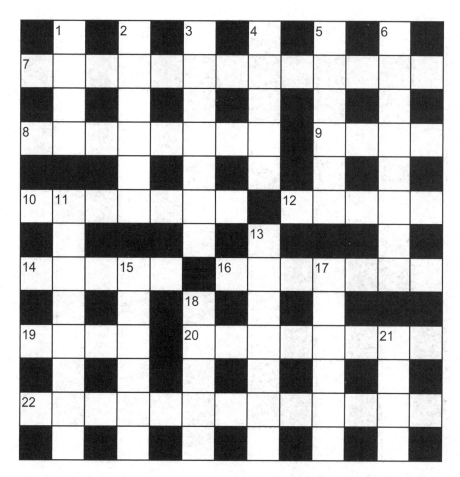

Across

7 Line that bounds a circle (13)
8 Revolted (8)
9 Large washing bowl (4)
10 Sourness (7)
12 Coiled curve (5)
14 Thin fogs (5)
16 Year in which wine was produced (7)
19 Frozen rain (4)
20 Humorous verse (8)
22 Not capable of being restrained (13)

Down

1 Blaze (4)
2 Long speech (6)
3 Good luck charms (7)
4 Gives a meal to (5)
5 Frail (6)
6 Severely critical (8)
11 Medieval knightly system (8)
13 Total weight of organisms (7)
15 Greater in height (6)
17 Oppressively hot (6)
18 Smudges (5)
21 Select from a large amount (4)

CROSSWORD 385

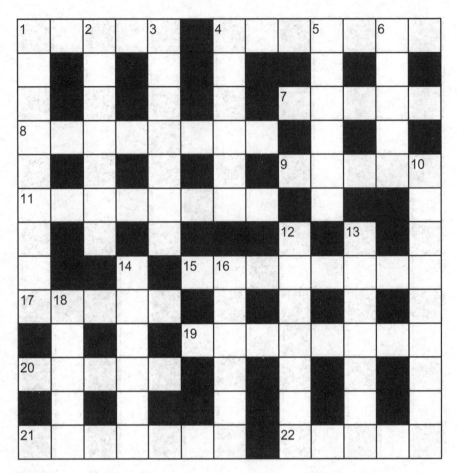

Across

1 Metal worker (5)
4 Modified (7)
7 Aromatic herb of the mint family (5)
8 Circumnavigating (8)
9 Recycle (5)
11 Reads out (8)
15 Similarity (8)
17 Range (5)
19 Opposites (8)
20 Danes (anag.) (5)
21 Comes into collision with (7)
22 Japanese mattress (5)

Down

1 Acuteness (9)
2 Dispensers (7)
3 Protective helmet (4,3)
4 Street (6)
5 Made a request to God (6)
6 Long poems derived from ancient tradition (5)
10 Violent release of energy (9)
12 Become less intense (4,3)
13 Nearest (7)
14 States as one's opinion (6)
16 Irritates (6)
18 Applaud (5)

Across

1 Poorly ventilated (6)

5 Glass container (6)

8 Caribbean country (4)

9 Unit of power (8)

10 Voting compartment (5)

11 Making a petition to God (7)

14 Respond aggressively to military action (7-6)

16 Evidence of disease (7)

18 Small sales stand (5)

20 Actor (8)

22 Aim or target (4)

23 Possessors (6)

24 Ordered arrangements (6)

Down

2 Necessarily true statement (9)

3 Squash (7)

4 Wooden crosspiece attached to animals (4)

5 Large root vegetable (8)

6 Raucous (5)

7 Lipid (3)

12 Essential (9)

13 Topsides (anag.) (8)

15 Part of a gun (7)

17 Moist stiff mixture (5)

19 ___ Kournikova: former tennis star (4)

21 In what way (3)

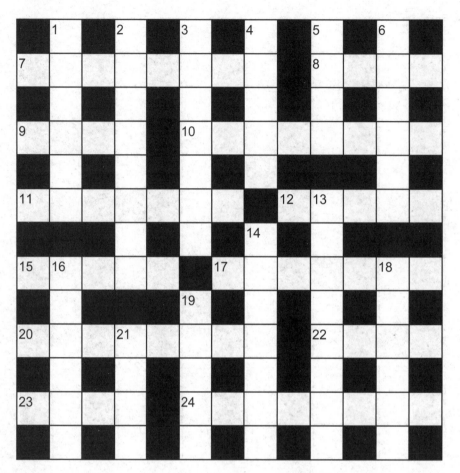

Across

7 Confirm (8)

8 Unwieldy ship (4)

9 Communicate purely using gestures (4)

10 The activities of government (8)

11 Faithfulness (7)

12 Equine animal (5)

15 Stared into space (5)

17 Country in South East Asia (7)

20 Pays homage to (8)

22 Area of a house (4)

23 Effervesce (4)

24 Stayed longer than necessary (8)

Down

1 Coarse cloth (6)

2 Able to read and write (8)

3 Floor coverings (7)

4 Gave out playing cards (5)

5 Hots (anag.) (4)

6 Pieces of bread (6)

13 Exclamations of protest (8)

14 Lost (7)

16 Infinitesimally small (6)

18 Makes amends for (6)

19 Charges (a sum of money) (5)

21 Relative extent (4)

Across

1 Rot or decay (of food) (6)
5 Hairpiece (3)
7 Value (5)
8 Miserly person (7)
9 Floral leaf (5)
10 Dishes that begin a meal (8)
12 Summing together (6)
14 E.g. March and May (6)
17 Where one parks the car (8)
18 Deceives or misleads (5)
20 Very long (7)
21 Stable compartment (5)
22 Obtained (3)
23 Commands (6)

Down

2 Exhilarated (7)
3 In a fair manner (8)
4 Hold tightly (4)
5 Stand for small objects (7)
6 Rides at speed (7)
7 Fatigued (5)
11 Memento (8)
12 Enduring (7)
13 Most profound (7)
15 Purple-flowered plant (7)
16 Adornment (5)
19 Absorbent pad (4)

CROSSWORD 389

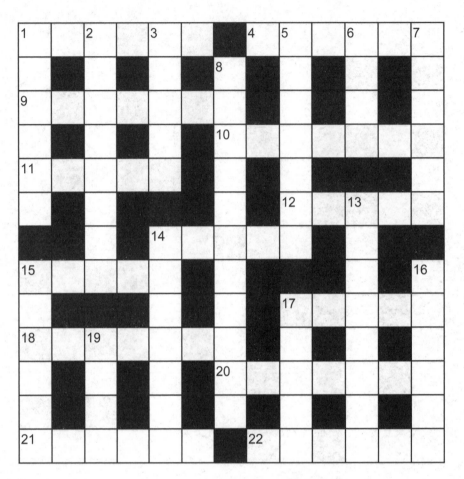

Across

1 Send away (6)
4 Journey by air (6)
9 Grow more mature (7)
10 Oceanic birds (7)
11 Green citrus fruits (5)
12 Reddish (5)
14 Fastened in position (5)
15 Smooth cream of vegetables (5)
17 Freedom from war (5)
18 Spiny anteater (7)
20 Striking lightly (7)
21 Safe place (6)
22 Causes a sharp pain (6)

Down

1 Corporal (6)
2 11th month of the year (8)
3 Seals (anag.) (5)
5 Garment worn by dancers (7)
6 Pierce with a horn (4)
7 Very reliable (6)
8 Not exact (11)
13 Length of time something lasts (8)
14 Giving food to (7)
15 Kitchen tool to remove vegetable skin (6)
16 Periods of rule (6)
17 Songbird (5)
19 Foot of a horse (4)

Across

7 Edible plant tuber (6)

8 Attempting (6)

9 Vale (4)

10 Wrinkled; creased (8)

11 Small brownish spot on the skin (7)

13 Waterslide (5)

15 Rise to one's feet (5)

16 Nation (7)

18 Sewed together (8)

19 Ill-mannered (4)

21 Silkworm covering (6)

22 Particles of sand (6)

Down

1 Make a hole in; drill (4)

2 Figment of the imagination (13)

3 Light spongy baked dish (7)

4 Agitates a liquid (5)

5 Valetudinarian (13)

6 Forebear (8)

12 Act of moving around an axis (8)

14 Dowager (anag.) (7)

17 Deliberate; cogitate (5)

20 Finished; complete (4)

CROSSWORD 391

Across

1 Cut of beef (4)
3 Small cigars (8)
9 Attacks (7)
10 Dubious (5)
11 Blasphemous (12)
14 Gallivant (3)
16 Store of hoarded wealth (5)
17 Consume a meal (3)
18 Gathering of people (12)
21 Assumed proposition (5)
22 Proportionately (3,4)
23 Extreme reproach (8)
24 Variety; sort (4)

Down

1 Redeploy (8)
2 Agreeable sound or tune (5)
4 Possesses (3)
5 Cooling device (12)
6 Vague and uncertain (7)
7 Utters (4)
8 Break up into pieces (12)
12 Decay (5)
13 Early period of human culture (5,3)
15 Bouncer (7)
19 European country (5)
20 Group of countries in an alliance (4)
22 Seed of an apple (3)

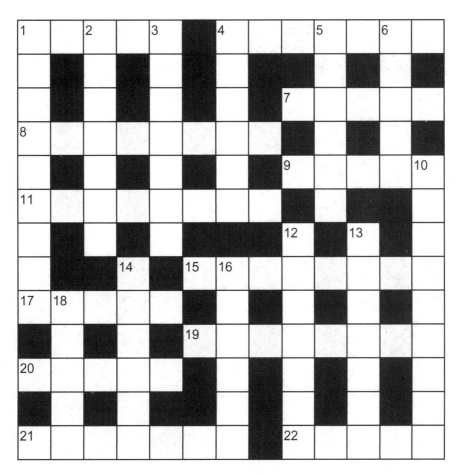

Across

1 Greets with enthusiasm (5)

4 Make blissfully happy (7)

7 Assembly (5)

8 Prayer (8)

9 Nonsense (5)

11 Closeness (8)

15 Extreme audacity (8)

17 Hand protector (5)

19 Strong dislike (8)

20 Starting point (5)

21 Pursuing (7)

22 Showered with love (5)

Down

1 Event (9)

2 In the place of (7)

3 Chairs (7)

4 Sweeping implements (6)

5 Lethargic (6)

6 Hurled (5)

10 Swapped (9)

12 Featured in the leading role (7)

13 Juicy soft fruit (7)

14 Keeps away from (6)

16 Owning (6)

18 Reluctant (5)

Across

1 Office table (4)
3 Cold Spanish tomato soup (8)
9 Stormy (7)
10 Type of military operation (5)
11 Appropriate (3)
12 Pierces with a horn (5)
13 Oarsman (5)
15 Egg-shaped solid (5)
17 Strangely (5)
18 Epoch (3)
19 Plant hormone (5)
20 Speak excitedly of (7)
21 Opposite of westerly (8)
22 Small amphibian (4)

Down

1 Unemotional (13)
2 Gush out in a jet (5)
4 In a careless manner (6)
5 Person studying after a first degree (12)
6 Easier to understand (7)
7 Exaggeration (13)
8 Ability to see the future (12)
14 Alphabetical lists (7)
16 Trying experience (6)
18 Severe (5)

Across

1 Irritable (3-8)
9 Explode (5)
10 Vitality (3)
11 Raves (5)
12 Regal (5)
13 Careless (8)
16 Damage (a reputation) (8)
18 Device that clears a car windscreen (5)
21 The Hunter (constellation) (5)
22 17th Greek letter (3)
23 Buyer (5)
24 Without guilt (11)

Down

2 Wash and iron (7)
3 Table support (7)
4 Cave openings (6)
5 Go inside (5)
6 Messenger (5)
7 Clay pottery (11)
8 Trifling sum of money (5,6)
14 Licentious (7)
15 Reaches a destination (7)
17 Calls to mind (6)
19 Explore or examine (5)
20 Quantitative relation between two amounts (5)

Across

1 Where one finds Tehran (4)
3 Photograph (8)
9 The North Star (7)
10 Red cosmetic powder (5)
11 Propel a boat (3)
12 Supply with food (5)
13 Come into direct contact with (5)
15 Extreme (5)
17 Mythical monster (5)
18 Pouch; enclosed space (3)
19 Musical note (5)
20 Small falcon (7)
21 Decorated with a raised design (8)
22 Askew (4)

Down

1 Very subtle (13)
2 Permit (5)
4 Capital of the Bahamas (6)
5 Provincialism (12)
6 Inhabited by ghosts (7)
7 Conceptually (13)
8 Productivity (12)
14 Saying (7)
16 Equipment for fishing (6)
18 Drinking tube (5)

Across

7 Coiffure (6)

8 Loves dearly (6)

9 Gradually deprive of milk (4)

10 Large amphibian (8)

11 Flashed on and off (7)

13 Water container; sink (5)

15 Suggest (5)

16 Questions (7)

18 Choosing to abstain from alcohol (8)

19 Bloodsucking arachnid (4)

21 Impart knowledge (6)

22 Embarrassing mistake (3-3)

Down

1 Broad blade; nave (anag.) (4)

2 Way of saying a word (13)

3 Multiplied by two (7)

4 Technical problem (5)

5 Intense fire (13)

6 Resembling a hare (8)

12 A detail to be explained (5,3)

14 Simple song for a baby (7)

17 Tree part left after it is cut down (5)

20 At a low temperature (4)

CROSSWORD 397

Across

1 Stagnant; lazy (4)
3 Glass-like volcanic rock (8)
9 Clap (7)
10 Symbol (5)
11 Type of statistical chart (3)
12 Settle for sleep (of birds) (5)
13 Looks after oneself (5)
15 Sceptic (5)
17 Machine; automaton (5)
18 Of a low standard (3)
19 Up and about (5)
20 Lessen (7)
21 Making certain of (8)
22 Poker stake (4)

Down

1 Not proper (13)
2 Momentary oversight (5)
4 Blunt needle (6)
5 Junction (12)
6 Annoying (7)
7 Failure to be present at (13)
8 Maker (12)
14 Discusses (7)
16 Wrestling hold (6)
18 Relay device (5)

Across

1 Undergo a hardship (6)
4 Academy Awards (6)
9 Cigarette constituent (7)
10 Convent (7)
11 Shrewd (5)
12 Alcoholic beverage (5)
14 Waterlogged area of land (5)
15 Destiny; fate (5)
17 Derisive smile (5)
18 Formal speech (7)
20 Agreed or corresponded (7)
21 Cooks over boiling water (6)
22 Barriers (6)

Down

1 Tempt (6)
2 Suave; stylish (8)
3 Unsteady (5)
5 Green vegetable (7)
6 Shaft on which a wheel rotates (4)
7 Woodcutter (6)
8 Restricted (11)
13 Relating to the home (8)
14 Highest amount (7)
15 Bumps into (6)
16 Classifies; sorts (6)
17 Foam or froth (5)
19 Having inherent ability (4)

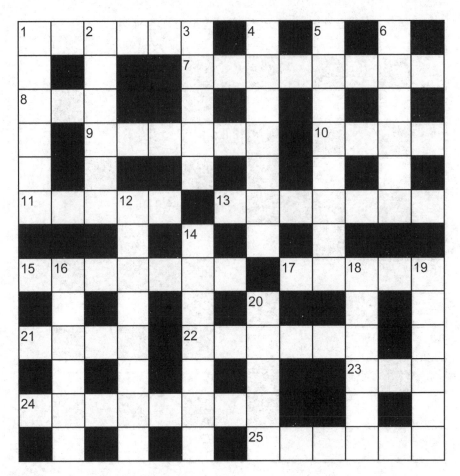

Across

1 Turn down (6)
7 Answered sharply (8)
8 Canine (3)
9 Mourn the loss of (6)
10 Seed containers (4)
11 Shrub fence (5)
13 Allots (7)
15 Tentacled cephalopod (7)
17 Commence (5)
21 Assist (4)
22 Scarcity (6)
23 Collection of paper (3)
24 Wanders (of a stream) (8)
25 Elapsed (of time) (6)

Down

1 Swollen edible root (6)
2 Pleaded with (6)
3 Cooked in hot fat (5)
4 Belief that there is no God (7)
5 Form of carbon (8)
6 Make less sensitive (6)
12 Putting into categories (8)
14 Rushes (7)
16 Masticated (6)
18 Sculptured symbols (6)
19 Indicated assent (6)
20 Understand (5)

Across

1 Finish (4)
3 Moment of great revelation (8)
9 Friendly (7)
10 Rule (5)
11 Mapmaker (12)
13 Reprimand (6)
15 Sour to the taste (6)
17 Tamed (12)
20 Main (5)
21 Soft metallic element (7)
22 Laughably small (8)
23 Extent of a surface (4)

Down

1 Stole; grabbed suddenly (8)
2 Make available for sale (5)
4 Metrical writing (6)
5 Shrewdness (12)
6 Eased in (anag.) (7)
7 Pull abruptly (4)
8 Completeness (12)
12 The scholastic world (8)
14 More spacious (7)
16 Less fresh (of bread) (6)
18 One who always puts in a lot of effort (5)
19 Imitated (4)

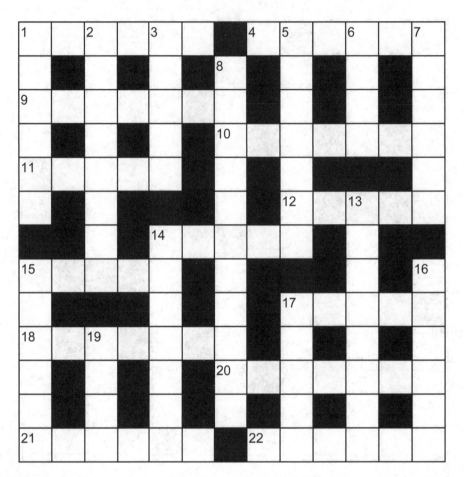

Across

1 Determine (6)

4 Fashions (6)

9 Hanging drapery (7)

10 Glisten (7)

11 Covered with powdery dirt (5)

12 Periods of 60 minutes (5)

14 Ancient measure of length (5)

15 Shady spot under trees (5)

17 Peak (5)

18 The giving up of rights (7)

20 Climbing plant (7)

21 Sharp reply (6)

22 Holds one's ground (6)

Down

1 Separate into pieces (6)

2 Cabbage salad (8)

3 Drab (5)

5 This evening (7)

6 Fertile type of soil (4)

7 Horses (anag.) (6)

8 Likeness (11)

13 Support (8)

14 Warship (7)

15 Investor (6)

16 Long-legged wading birds (6)

17 Fastening device (5)

19 Chair (4)

Across

1 Periods of history (6)
5 Public square in Italy (6)
8 Ewer (anag.) (4)
9 Variants (8)
10 Indian garments (5)
11 Letter (7)
14 Tyrannical; domineering (13)
16 Crying (7)
18 Capable of flowing (5)
20 Wild flower (8)
22 Bucket (4)
23 Gets rid of (6)
24 Farewell remark (3-3)

Down

2 Too early (9)
3 Value greatly (7)
4 Salvage (4)
5 Low walls at balcony edges (8)
6 Operatic songs (5)
7 School of Mahayana Buddhism (3)
12 Legal responsibility for something (9)
13 Daughter of a sovereign (8)
15 Fall back (7)
17 Annoy (5)
19 Heavy stick used as a weapon (4)
21 Illumination unit (3)

CROSSWORD 403

Across

1 Bring about using artifice (8)
5 Platform leading out to sea (4)
9 Waterlogged ground (5)
10 Joins together (5)
11 Skilled in doing something (10)
14 Entrance hall (6)
15 Walk laboriously (6)
17 Book written by hand (10)
20 Japanese form of fencing (5)
21 Not asleep (5)
22 Long grass (4)
23 Cause to feel isolated (8)

Down

1 Apex or peak (4)
2 Ark builder (4)
3 Consequence of an event (12)
4 Slander; disparage (6)
6 Suggestive remark (8)
7 Flower-shaped competition awards (8)
8 Coat with a metal (12)
12 Cartographer (8)
13 Mounted guns (8)
16 Relating to a wedding (6)
18 Mother (4)
19 Allot a punishment (4)

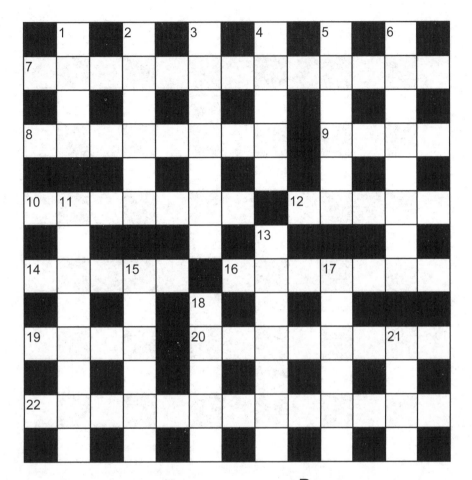

Across

7 Miscellaneous equipment (13)
8 Mentally sharp (8)
9 Financial penalty (4)
10 Person who bargains (7)
12 State of nervous excitement (5)
14 Discharged a weapon (5)
16 Consume by fire (7)
19 Complain unreasonably; fish (4)
20 Fighters (8)
22 Type of traditional photography (5-3-5)

Down

1 Futile (4)
2 Moving swiftly (6)
3 Prospered (7)
4 Liberates (5)
5 Talk nonsense (6)
6 Trailblazers (8)
11 In a friendly manner (8)
13 Companion (7)
15 Anticipate (6)
17 Plant disease (6)
18 Pinch; squeeze (5)
21 Mud grooves (4)

CROSSWORD 405

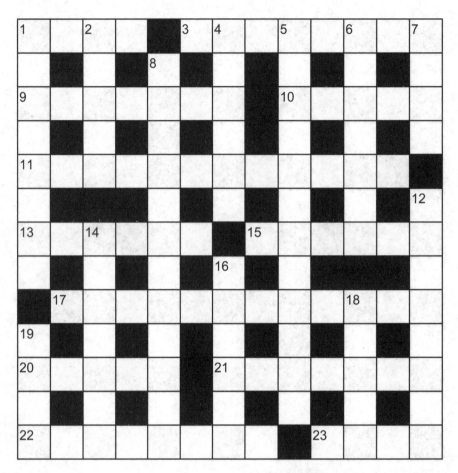

Across

1 Manure (4)
3 Legal ambiguity (8)
9 Variety show (7)
10 Country in North East Africa (5)
11 Formal notice (12)
13 Son of Daedalus in Greek mythology (6)
15 Limper (anag.) (6)
17 Coming between two things (12)
20 Small piece of land (5)
21 Not level (7)
22 Transporting by hand (8)
23 Document of ownership (4)

Down

1 Person who repairs cars (8)
2 Private room on a ship (5)
4 The science of light (6)
5 What p.m. stands for (4,8)
6 A number defining position (7)
7 Sea eagle (4)
8 Deceitfully (12)
12 Driven to action (8)
14 Ring-shaped (7)
16 Call into question (6)
18 Entertain (5)
19 Metallic element (4)

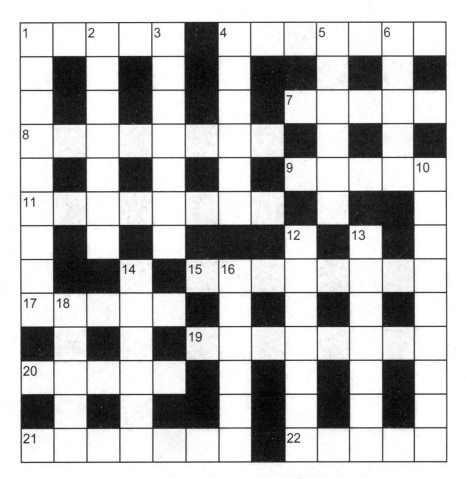

Across

1 Planet (5)
4 Residential areas (7)
7 Hiding place (5)
8 Very happy (8)
9 Pertaining to the Netherlands (5)
11 Secured; tied (8)
15 Stressed (8)
17 Secreting organ (5)
19 Intelligentsia (8)
20 Declares (5)
21 Sterile (7)
22 Amounts of medicine (5)

Down

1 Symbol of surrender (5,4)
2 Remedy (7)
3 Bored (7)
4 Ball-shaped object (6)
5 False (6)
6 Staple (5)
10 Appears as the star of the show (9)
12 Highly excited (7)
13 Seeks to hurt (7)
14 Catch or snare (6)
16 One who judges a literary work (6)
18 Resides (5)

CROSSWORD 407

Across

1 Self-satisfied (4)
3 Food enhancer (8)
9 Limiest (anag.) (7)
10 Eighth Greek letter (5)
11 Cairo is in this country (5)
12 Conjuring up feelings (7)
13 Slender candles (6)
15 Street musician (6)
17 Join in an activity (7)
18 Faith in another (5)
20 Determine the number of (5)
21 Dressed in a vestment (7)
22 Set free (8)
23 Solely (4)

Down

1 Lacking originality (13)
2 Oneness (5)
4 More moist (6)
5 Preliminary (12)
6 Tool that is useful for the Arctic (3,4)
7 In an inflated manner (13)
8 Sound of quick light steps (6-6)
14 Agitate (7)
16 Opposite of a victory (6)
19 Living in a city (5)

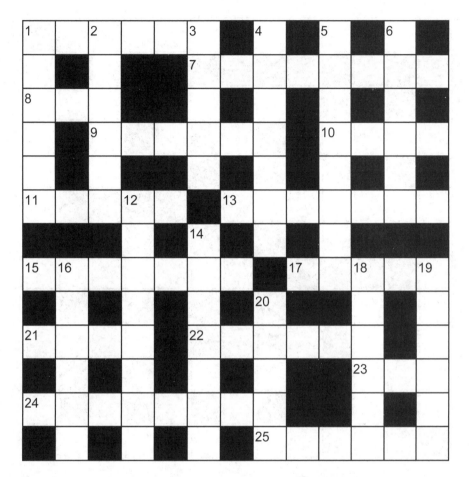

Across

1 Spoken form of communication (6)
7 Diligence (8)
8 Single in number (3)
9 Accident (6)
10 Small children (4)
11 Stead (anag.) (5)
13 Large flightless bird (7)
15 Portentous (7)
17 Twenty (5)
21 Ingredient in vegetarian cooking (4)
22 Too many to be counted (6)
23 Mixture of gases we breathe (3)
24 Sinking down (8)
25 Organic compounds (6)

Down

1 Ought to (6)
2 Free from a liability (6)
3 Opposite of lows (5)
4 Used for the storage of fat (of tissue) (7)
5 Recondite (8)
6 Very cold (of weather) (6)
12 Person implementing a will (8)
14 Fractional part (7)
16 Love affairs (6)
18 One's twilight years (3,3)
19 Background actors (6)
20 Raised floor or platform (5)

Across

1 Frustrating (11)
9 Type of bandage (5)
10 Annoy (3)
11 Rise (3,2)
12 Corrodes (5)
13 Opposite of hardness (8)
16 Eye condition (8)
18 Travels on a bicycle (5)
21 Long for (5)
22 Limb (3)
23 Retrieve (5)
24 Founded (11)

Down

2 Please or delight (7)
3 Reply (7)
4 States an opinion (6)
5 Big cat (5)
6 Metal spikes (5)
7 Dictatorial (11)
8 Very tall buildings (11)
14 Animal cages (7)
15 Love; genre of fiction (7)
17 Horizontal supporting beam (6)
19 Curbs; muffles (5)
20 Capital of Bulgaria (5)

Across

7 Rule with authority (6)

8 Measuring sticks (6)

9 Hurl missiles at (4)

10 Native of the United States (8)

11 Side of a coin bearing the head (7)

13 Card game (5)

15 Talons (5)

16 Engage in merrymaking (7)

18 Diabolical (8)

19 Solid; not soft (4)

21 Technique (6)

22 Jeans (6)

Down

1 Sector (4)

2 Boxing class division (13)

3 All together (2,5)

4 E.g. used a towel (5)

5 Legerdemain (7,2,4)

6 State of the USA (8)

12 Accepts to be true (8)

14 Untanned leather (7)

17 Wraps closely around (5)

20 Raised edges (4)

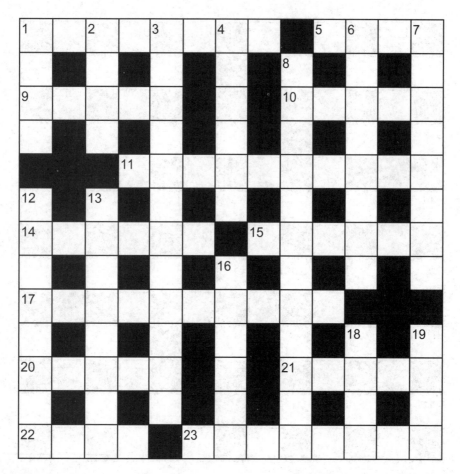

Across

1 Muddled (8)

5 Enclose in paper (4)

9 Confusion (3-2)

10 Debate in a heated manner (5)

11 Security for a loan (10)

14 Continue to exist (6)

15 Companion (6)

17 Displease (10)

20 Quavering sound (5)

21 Plentiful (5)

22 Floor coverings (4)

23 Copied (8)

Down

1 Arrive (4)

2 Immediately following (4)

3 Making no money (12)

4 Envelop (6)

6 Took into account (8)

7 Make impossible (8)

8 Unemotional and practical (6-2-4)

12 Animal that hunts (8)

13 Wonderful (8)

16 Sagacity (6)

18 Narrow point of land projecting into water (4)

19 Geek (4)

Across

7 Implement change (6)

8 Small songbirds (6)

9 Short hollow thud (4)

10 Flight of steps (8)

11 Perfumed (7)

13 Ruin (5)

15 Deluge (5)

16 Part of an orchestra (7)

18 Surpass (8)

19 Lean (4)

21 Wirelesses (6)

22 Admit openly (6)

Down

1 Flat-bottomed boat (4)

2 Friendship (13)

3 Broke into pieces (7)

4 Spread out (5)

5 Act of taking for one's own use (13)

6 Robbing (8)

12 Pertaining to the arts (8)

14 Temporary measure (7)

17 Common plant (5)

20 Fine open fabric (4)

CROSSWORD 413

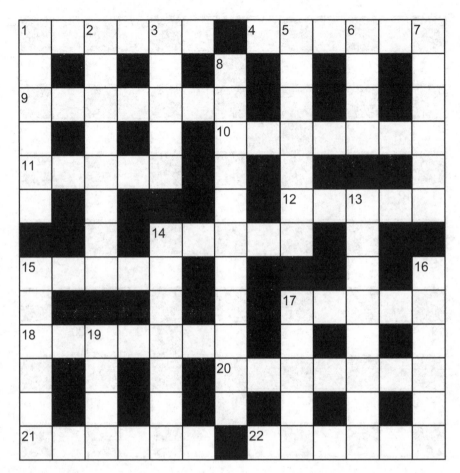

Across

1 Small folds in clothing (6)
4 Simple; unrefined (6)
9 Call the validity of a practice into question (7)
10 Comes back (7)
11 Selected (5)
12 Tall and slim (5)
14 Nose of an animal (5)
15 Hazy (5)
17 Attach to (5)
18 State of the USA (7)
20 Supply (7)
21 Meaner (anag.) (6)
22 Happen again (6)

Down

1 King's son (6)
2 Considers an option (8)
3 Follow the position of (5)
5 Arrogant person (7)
6 Level in a hierarchy (4)
7 Dry and brittle (of food) (6)
8 Accurate timer (11)
13 Midday (8)
14 Word having a similar meaning (7)
15 Complainer (6)
16 Scope (6)
17 Isolated (5)
19 Type of golf club (4)

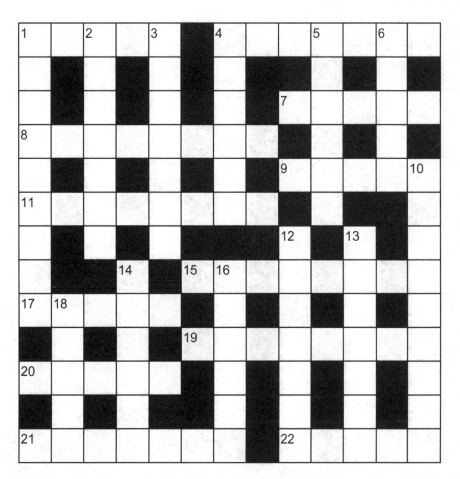

Across

1 Summed together (5)
4 Excluding (7)
7 Area of land (5)
8 Monarchist (8)
9 Sound loudly (5)
11 Scornful negativity (8)
15 Extravagant fuss (8)
17 Carnivorous mammal of the weasel family (5)
19 Mild aversion (8)
20 Brief burst of bright light (5)
21 Shows again (7)
22 Ascends (5)

Down

1 Natives of the United States (9)
2 Declaring to be untrue (7)
3 Cause to deviate (7)
4 Wild animals (6)
5 Seldom (6)
6 More pleasant (5)
10 Mistaken (9)
12 Slide (7)
13 Long-bladed hand tools (7)
14 Shrub with glossy leaves (6)
16 Comes up (6)
18 Diacritical mark (5)

CROSSWORD 415

Across

1 Supernatural (6)
5 Young bear (3)
7 Soft paste (5)
8 Nevertheless (7)
9 Very strong winds (5)
10 Looking up to (8)
12 Remove silt from a river (6)
14 Arm joints (6)
17 Large cask (8)
18 Studies a subject at university (5)
20 Brings about (7)
21 Good sense; reasoning (5)
22 Small winged insect (3)
23 Game bird; grumble (6)

Down

2 Rich fish soup (7)
3 Use something to maximum advantage (8)
4 Male deer (4)
5 One-eyed giant (7)
6 Turns red with embarrassment (7)
7 Cut back a tree (5)
11 Campaigner (8)
12 Question after a mission (7)
13 To the same degree (7)
15 Makes a journey (7)
16 Humorous (5)
19 Indication (4)

Across

1 Wrinkle; fold (6)
4 Dung beetle (6)
9 More jolly (7)
10 Angers (7)
11 Arrives (5)
12 Loots (anag.) (5)
14 Ordered arrangement (5)
15 Leaps (5)
17 Recently made (5)
18 Porch (7)
20 Large Israeli city (3,4)
21 Basic character of something (6)
22 Small piece of food (6)

Down

1 Light volcanic rock (6)
2 Metallic element (8)
3 Leaves (5)
5 Institution that raises money for the needy (7)
6 Peal (4)
7 Breaks open (6)
8 Act evasively (11)
13 Notes; sees (8)
14 Into parts (7)
15 Pertaining to Jupiter (6)
16 Type of spade (6)
17 Leaf of parchment (5)
19 Destroy (4)

Across

1 Exclamation of relief (4)
3 Terrible (8)
9 No longer in existence (7)
10 Strong ringing sound (5)
11 Working for oneself (4-8)
14 Annoy constantly (3)
16 Juicy fruit (5)
17 Level golf score (3)
18 Showed not to be true (12)
21 Scorch (5)
22 Movement of vehicles en masse (7)
23 Arithmetic operation (8)
24 Poses a question (4)

Down

1 Agreeable (8)
2 Praise enthusiastically (5)
4 Rodent (3)
5 Extremely large (12)
6 Sudden outburst of something (5-2)
7 Light toboggan (4)
8 Sporadic (12)
12 Mammal that eats bamboo (5)
13 Manufactures (8)
15 Moaned (7)
19 Bunches (5)
20 One of the continents (4)
22 Excessively (3)

Across

7 Figure of speech (8)

8 Not at home (4)

9 Not stereo (4)

10 State of feeling safe (8)

11 Marks of a zebra (7)

12 Move to music (5)

15 Measuring instrument (5)

17 Injurious (7)

20 Reprimanding (8)

22 Manner of walking (4)

23 Self-righteous person (4)

24 Throwing out (8)

Down

1 Obtain by coercion (6)

2 Formidable; impressive (8)

3 Long locks of hair (7)

4 Small cut (5)

5 Equitable (4)

6 Adhesive putty (6)

13 Supreme being (8)

14 Chuckled (7)

16 Agreement (6)

18 Workers' groups (6)

19 Game similar to handball (5)

21 Gels (anag.) (4)

CROSSWORD 419

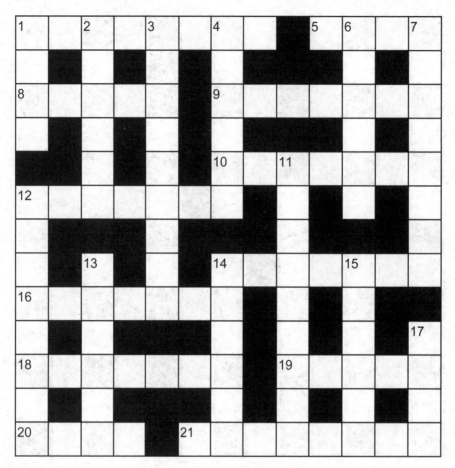

Across

1 Grace (8)
5 Unit of land area (4)
8 Extreme fear (5)
9 Due to the fact that (7)
10 Laughable (7)
12 Bestowing; conferring (7)
14 Uncovers (7)
16 Steeps in liquid (7)
18 Form a mental picture (7)
19 Pertaining to the ear (5)
20 Spun thread used for knitting (4)
21 Judges (8)

Down

1 Ceases (4)
2 Constructs a building (6)
3 Fearless; very bold (9)
4 Being with organic and
   cybernetic parts (6)
6 Round and plump (6)
7 Critical explanation (8)
11 Arouse interest in (9)
12 Masculinity (8)
13 Matter (6)
14 Rhesus (anag.) (6)
15 Refrains from injuring (6)
17 Money given to the poor (4)

Across

1 Noon (6)
4 Impress deeply (6)
9 Create a positive feeling in a person (7)
10 Civil action brought to court (7)
11 Late (5)
12 Hazardous; dangerous (5)
14 Fits of violent anger (5)
15 At that place; not here (5)
17 Mournful song (5)
18 Declare to be true (7)
20 One who eats a bit at a time (7)
21 Elegant and slender (6)
22 Heavy food (6)

Down

1 Small portion or share (6)
2 Explain using words (8)
3 Friendship (5)
5 Responses (7)
6 Domesticated ox (4)
7 Hearty (anag.) (6)
8 Hostile and aggressive (11)
13 Surprised (8)
14 Let in again (7)
15 Strong ringing sounds (6)
16 Decide with authority (6)
17 First appearance (5)
19 Hard green gem (4)

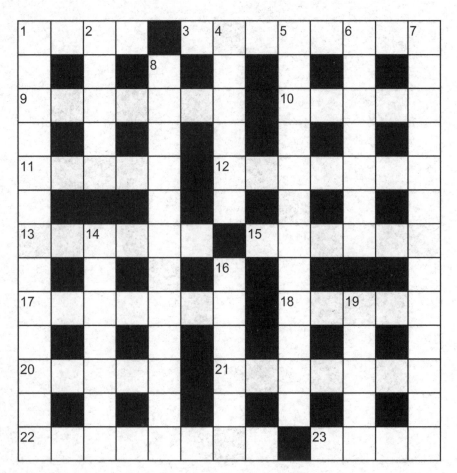

Across

1 Reverse (4)
3 Obscures the light from a celestial body (8)
9 Philosophical theory (7)
10 Lived (anag.) (5)
11 Of the moon (5)
12 Poisonous metallic element (7)
13 Consider to be true (6)
15 Composite fungus and alga (6)
17 Fatuously (7)
18 Venomous snake (5)
20 Topic (5)
21 Waterproof fabric (7)
22 Boating (8)
23 Parched (4)

Down

1 Lack of dependability (13)
2 Draw off liquid from (5)
4 Fighting between armed forces (6)
5 Dimly; not clearly (12)
6 Next after sixth (7)
7 Complete in itself (of a thing) (4-9)
8 Give a false account of (12)
14 Traditional example (7)
16 Wealthy person in business (6)
19 One who makes bread (5)

Across

1 Complain (4)
3 Elks idea (anag.) (8)
9 Child's room (7)
10 Moved slowly (5)
11 Craze (3)
12 Smell (5)
13 Female sovereign (5)
15 Follow on from (5)
17 Individual things (5)
18 Constrictor snake (3)
19 Escape from (5)
20 Please immensely (7)
21 Flowering plant (5,3)
22 Disgust with an excess of sweetness (4)

Down

1 Makers (13)
2 Exposed (5)
4 A person in general (6)
5 Capable of being traded (12)
6 Freezing (3-4)
7 Wastefully; lavishly (13)
8 Having a tendency to become liquid (12)
14 Connoisseur; gourmet (7)
16 Quash; tame (6)
18 Ring-shaped roll (5)

CROSSWORD 423

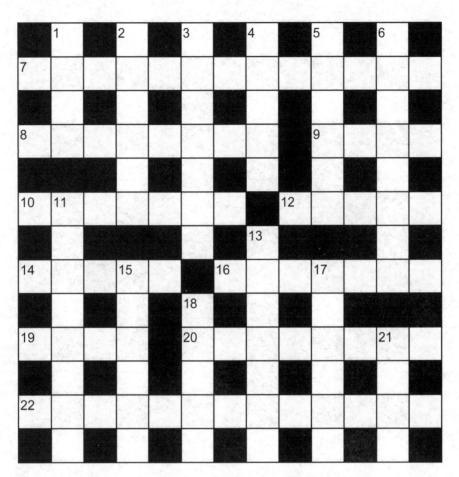

Across

7 Philosophy of law (13)
8 Sergeant (anag.) (8)
9 Hide underground (4)
10 Combatant (7)
12 Worked steadily at (5)
14 Wheels that move rudders on ships (5)
16 People who tend cattle (7)
19 Reasons; explanations (4)
20 In the open air (8)
22 Institution (13)

Down

1 Really big (4)
2 Person who strongly resembles another (6)
3 Financial supporter (7)
4 Courageous (5)
5 Oral (6)
6 Barely (8)
11 Purple quartz (8)
13 Warmest (7)
15 Misplace (6)
17 Flowers (6)
18 Screams like a wolf (5)
21 Smallest pig of the litter (4)

Across

1 Excessively (6)
5 Woody plants (6)
8 Sell (anag.) (4)
9 Striking noisily (8)
10 Cabs (5)
11 State of being twisted (7)
14 Forger (13)
16 Lines of equal pressure on maps (7)
18 Cooks slowly in liquid (5)
20 Sharp heel (8)
22 Negative votes (4)
23 More than is necessary (6)
24 Continue (6)

Down

2 E.g. Vesuvius and Etna (9)
3 E.g. from Moscow (7)
4 Ox-like mammals (4)
5 People who act pretentiously (4-4)
6 Garden tools (5)
7 Disallow (3)
12 Be too strong for (9)
13 Debris (8)
15 Aims or purposes (7)
17 Attractive young lady (5)
19 Ill-mannered person (4)
21 A man's dinner jacket (abbrev.) (3)

CROSSWORD 425

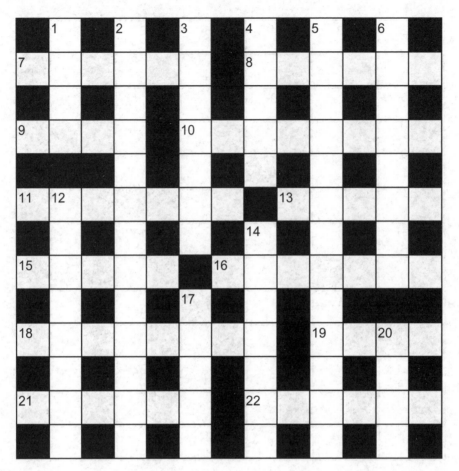

Across

7 Indicate (6)
8 Cause to remember (6)
9 Turn over (4)
10 Absurd representation of something (8)
11 Prepare beforehand (7)
13 Hard rock (5)
15 Diminishes (5)
16 Lived (7)
18 Light from our star (8)
19 Small rodents (4)
21 Using all one's resources (3,3)
22 River in Europe (6)

Down

1 Meat from a calf (4)
2 Understanding (13)
3 Long-haired hunting dogs (7)
4 Very untypical (5)
5 Ornamentation (13)
6 Example (8)
12 Obscurely (8)
14 Surpasses (7)
17 Right (anag.) (5)
20 Taxis (4)

Across

1 Always in a similar role (of an actor) (8)
5 Female child (4)
9 Broaden (5)
10 Apportions a punishment (5)
11 Act of making known (10)
14 Each (6)
15 Moon goddess in Greek mythology (6)
17 Companionship (10)
20 Wooden pin used to join surfaces together (5)
21 Lift with effort (5)
22 Titled peer (4)
23 Scholarly (8)

Down

1 Pulls a vehicle (4)
2 Fleshes out unnecessarily (4)
3 In a persuasive manner (12)
4 Stink (6)
6 An unwelcome person; invader (8)
7 Heard (8)
8 Made poor (12)
12 Yellow flower (8)
13 Conflict internal to a country (5,3)
16 Support; help (6)
18 Type of starch (4)
19 Beseeches (4)

Across

1 Shipment (11)
9 Targeted (5)
10 Pledge (3)
11 Annoying insects (5)
12 Fortune-telling card (5)
13 Remedy to a poison (8)
16 Lover (8)
18 Water-filled ditches around castles (5)
21 Faint southern constellation (5)
22 Part of a pen (3)
23 Large waterbirds (5)
24 Testimony (11)

Down

2 Corpulence (7)
3 Beach area (7)
4 Ploy (6)
5 In the middle of (5)
6 Not at all (5)
7 Act of making peace (11)
8 European country (11)
14 Hottest (7)
15 Cyclone (7)
17 Silver (literary) (6)
19 Head monk (5)
20 Smooth transition (5)

Across

1 Distinct sentence part (6)
4 Expresses one's opinion (6)
9 Country in northwestern Africa (7)
10 Atomic particle (7)
11 Devices that emit light (5)
12 Gasps (5)
14 Emerge from an egg (5)
15 Recipient of money (5)
17 Thorax (5)
18 Walked upon (7)
20 Loving deeply (7)
21 Without difficulty (6)
22 Alcove (6)

Down

1 Mammals with humps (6)
2 Ill feeling (8)
3 Draws into the mouth (5)
5 Victory (7)
6 Rip up (4)
7 Very holy people (6)
8 Not absolute (11)
13 Plummet (8)
14 Attentive (7)
15 Small and dainty (6)
16 Raised platforms (6)
17 Laborious task (5)
19 Is indebted to pay (4)

CROSSWORD 429

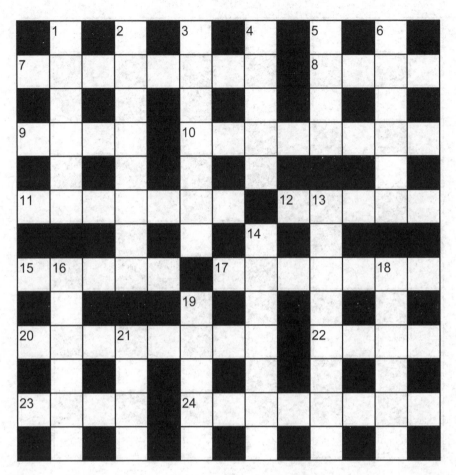

Across

7 Vehicle with three wheels (8)
8 Owl cry (4)
9 Tall cereal grass (4)
10 Opposite of a pessimist (8)
11 Primarily (7)
12 Inferior to (5)
15 Search a person; leap playfully (5)
17 Satisfy; conciliate (7)
20 Tripped up (8)
22 Pointer on a clock (4)
23 Steep and rugged rock (4)
24 Read out loud (8)

Down

1 Decorative ornament (6)
2 Airport checking devices (8)
3 Learning institutions (7)
4 Openings for air; outlets (5)
5 Fancy (4)
6 Work chiefs (6)
13 In the sky (8)
14 Arachnids (7)
16 Yield or make (a profit) (6)
18 Poem of fourteen lines (6)
19 Mix smoothly (5)
21 Foolish people (informal) (4)

Across

1 Well-mannered (5)
4 Dull (7)
7 Reduces one's speed (5)
8 Express as a number (8)
9 Restraining straps (5)
11 Infinite time (8)
15 Person who campaigns for political change (8)
17 Tends (anag.) (5)
19 Part of a house (8)
20 Heavy noble gas (5)
21 Rider (7)
22 Give a solemn oath (5)

Down

1 Vanquished (9)
2 Wild (of an animal) (7)
3 Stopping (7)
4 Outsider (6)
5 Melodious (6)
6 Certain to fail (2-3)
10 Month (9)
12 Codes (7)
13 Retaliatory action (7)
14 Walk casually (6)
16 Item of neckwear (6)
18 Mournful poem (5)

CROSSWORD 431

Across

1 True information (4)
3 Against the current (8)
9 People who make money (7)
10 Urge into action (5)
11 Former name of the Democratic Republic of Congo (5)
12 Derived from living matter (7)
13 Subtle detail (6)
15 Wall painting; mural (6)
17 Flat highland (7)
18 Cinders (5)
20 Lazes; does nothing (5)
21 Erase or remove (7)
22 Delaying (8)
23 Sight organs (4)

Down

1 Temperature at which water turns to ice (8,5)
2 Breed of dog (5)
4 Points (anag.) (6)
5 Reckless; ready to react violently (7-5)
6 Uses up energy (7)
7 Spite (13)
8 Incessantly (12)
14 Obsequious person (7)
16 Deep serving dish (6)
19 Useful (5)

Across

7 Telephone part containing the earpiece (8)
8 Greasy (4)
9 Injure (4)
10 Built in a certain place (8)
11 Merit (7)
12 Burst of light (5)
15 Frozen dew (5)
17 Loquacious (7)
20 Doorway (8)
22 Italian acknowledgement (4)
23 Left side of a ship (4)
24 At all; of any kind (8)

Down

1 Decline to do something (6)
2 Small falcons (8)
3 Elusive (7)
4 Beast (5)
5 Settee (4)
6 Extraterrestrials (6)
13 Propels with force (8)
14 Supervisory worker (7)
16 Without pattern (6)
18 Rents out (6)
19 Bites at persistently (5)
21 Decays (4)

Across

1 Set of instructions (6)
7 Period during which you live (8)
8 How (anag.) (3)
9 Clock or watch mechanism (6)
10 Associate (4)
11 Sediment (5)
13 Study of the body (7)
15 Give up (7)
17 Legendary stories (5)
21 Brown meat quickly (4)
22 Toy that is shaken (6)
23 Cry of a cat (3)
24 Shiny; sparkly (8)
25 Day of rest (6)

Down

1 Opposite of fast forward (6)
2 Look through casually (6)
3 Lumps of earth (5)
4 Offend the modesty of (7)
5 Furtive (8)
6 Symbol or representation (6)
12 Make; produce (8)
14 Wooed (7)
16 Insect of the order Coleoptera (6)
18 Swarmed (6)
19 Tunnel under a road for pedestrians (6)
20 Remains (5)

Across

7 Musical interval (8)

8 Nocturnal birds of prey (4)

9 Feeling of hunger (4)

10 Conventional (8)

11 Expression of regret (7)

12 Merchandise; possessions (5)

15 Becomes acrimonious (5)

17 Altitudes (7)

20 Adult male horse (8)

22 E.g. pecan and cashew (4)

23 Animate existence (4)

24 Beat easily (8)

Down

1 Depart suddenly (6)

2 Remarkable (8)

3 Administrative division (7)

4 Fleshy (5)

5 Game played on horseback (4)

6 Nut-like seed that marzipan is made from (6)

13 Living thing (8)

14 Act of going back in (2-5)

16 Make a larger offer at auction (6)

18 Restraint (6)

19 Reverence for God (5)

21 Right to hold property (4)

CROSSWORD 435

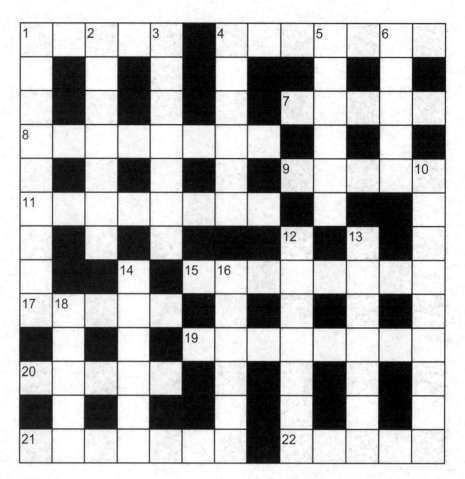

Across

1 Diving waterbird (5)
4 Gives satisfaction (7)
7 Succulent (5)
8 Clear (8)
9 Stomach (5)
11 Pear-shaped fruits native to Mexico (8)
15 Fast runner (8)
17 Swallowed liquid (5)
19 Neutral particle with negligible mass (8)
20 Length of interlaced hair (5)
21 Upward slopes (7)
22 Teams (5)

Down

1 Left university with a degree (9)
2 Act of avoiding capture (7)
3 Morally right (7)
4 Mexican cloak (6)
5 Entertained (6)
6 Do really well at (5)
10 Annuals (9)
12 Cylinders found in engines (7)
13 Marked like a zebra (7)
14 Not ready to eat (of fruit) (6)
16 Portions (6)
18 Parts in a play (5)

Across

1 Quartz-like gem (4)
3 Adhering to closely (8)
9 Livid (7)
10 Opposite of lower (5)
11 Building (12)
13 Paired (anag.) (6)
15 Collapse (4,2)
17 Unfriendly (12)
20 Work spirit (5)
21 E.g. from Rome (7)
22 Fretting (8)
23 Part of the foot (4)

Down

1 People holding positions of authority (8)
2 Protective garment worn in the kitchen (5)
4 Fine cloth (6)
5 Military judicial body (5,7)
6 Beseech (7)
7 Encircle or bind (4)
8 Luckily (12)
12 Occurring within (8)
14 Leopard (7)
16 Choice (6)
18 Newly-wed (5)
19 Cry of a cat (4)

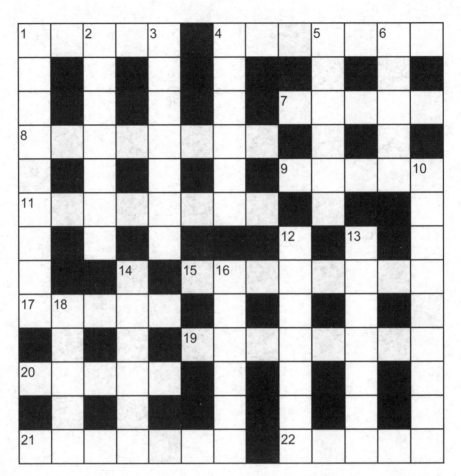

Across

1 Irritate (5)
4 Granite (anag.) (7)
7 Walk (5)
8 Fail to notice (8)
9 Makes a garment from wool (5)
11 Planned (8)
15 Pertaining to Spain (8)
17 Milky fluid found in some plants (5)
19 Stronghold (8)
20 Dull car sounds (5)
21 Got away (7)
22 Tree of the birch family (5)

Down

1 Relating to the stomach (9)
2 Originality (7)
3 Screaming (7)
4 Pay no attention to (6)
5 Very enthusiastic (6)
6 Browned bread (5)
10 Person that follows (9)
12 Kitchen implement (7)
13 Segmented worm (7)
14 Figure of speech (6)
16 Pressed clothes (6)
18 Yearns for (5)

Across

1 Pursued (6)
5 Money received (6)
8 Projecting edge (4)
9 Where one finds Harare (8)
10 Road information boards (5)
11 Sculptures (7)
14 Assemblage (13)
16 Compel by coercion (7)
18 Abominable snowmen (5)
20 Criminal (8)
22 Reduces in length (4)
23 Positively charged atomic particle (6)
24 Twist suddenly (6)

Down

2 Herald (9)
3 Strongly influencing later developments (7)
4 Sleep lightly (4)
5 Not ripe (of fruit) (8)
6 Seashore (5)
7 Throat of a voracious animal (3)
12 Vain (9)
13 Give courage (8)
15 Molasses (7)
17 Big (5)
19 Make beer or ale (4)
21 Pro (3)

Across

1 Stage of twilight (4)
3 State of the USA (8)
9 Novice driver (7)
10 Bed covering (5)
11 Contests (12)
13 Stylish; high quality (6)
15 Taxonomic groupings (6)
17 Generally accepted (12)
20 Promotional wording (5)
21 Open-meshed material (7)
22 Walked unsteadily (8)
23 Sell (4)

Down

1 Highly desirable food item (8)
2 Involuntary muscle contraction (5)
4 Small insect (6)
5 Demands or needs (12)
6 E.g. biology (7)
7 Creative disciplines (4)
8 Not guided by good sense (12)
12 Secured with a dressing (8)
14 Report of an event (7)
16 Sharp pain (6)
18 Steer (5)
19 Tuba (anag.) (4)

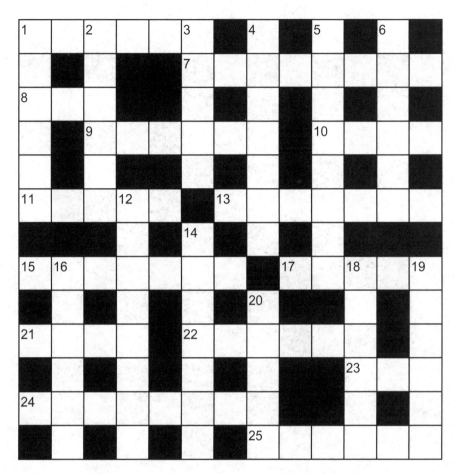

Across

1 Measure of capacity for corn (6)
7 Amaze (8)
8 Belonging to us (3)
9 One who has a salary (6)
10 Building covering (4)
11 Grip tightly; steal (5)
13 Young children (7)
15 Secretion of an endocrine gland (7)
17 Local authority rule (2-3)
21 Small bottle (4)
22 Black Sea peninsula (6)
23 Definite article (3)
24 Person with an appreciation of beauty (8)
25 Missing human interaction (6)

Down

1 Fill a balloon with air (4,2)
2 Television surface (6)
3 Areas of mown grass (5)
4 Gazing (7)
5 Supplication (8)
6 Classify (6)
12 Gather together and merge (8)
14 Device attached to a door (7)
16 Thought; supposed (6)
18 Hate (6)
19 Wet (6)
20 Tiny part of an image (5)

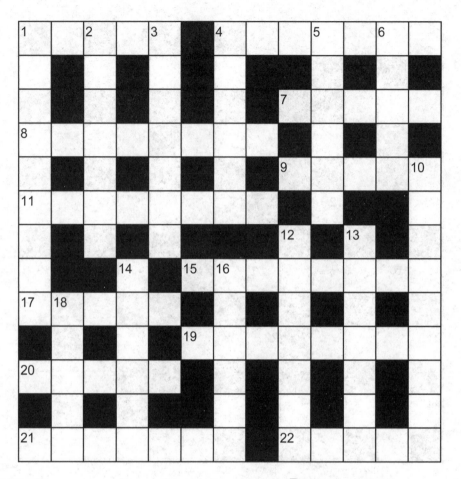

Across

1 Conveyed by gestures (5)

4 Abundant (7)

7 Special reward (5)

8 Familiar description for a person (8)

9 Humped ruminant (5)

11 Predict the future (8)

15 Gruesome; morbid (8)

17 Prickly (5)

19 Almond paste (8)

20 Small game bird (5)

21 Feeling of vexation (7)

22 Entrance barriers (5)

Down

1 Makes larger (9)

2 Eyelash cosmetic (7)

3 Composed or serious manner (7)

4 Fundamental; essential (6)

5 Conventional (6)

6 Remove hair (5)

10 Gentleness of touch (9)

12 Making the sound of a bee (7)

13 Where you go to catch a flight (7)

14 Popular winter sport (6)

16 Abode of God (6)

18 Lavish (5)

Across

1 Small symbol or graphic (4)

3 Shackle (8)

9 Let out (7)

10 Woodland god (5)

11 Vital plant juice (3)

12 Burning (5)

13 Active cause (5)

15 Earnings (5)

17 Food relish (5)

18 Every (3)

19 Confuse or obscure (5)

20 Lift up (7)

21 Full of interesting happenings (8)

22 Resistance unit (pl.) (4)

Down

1 Untrustworthy (13)

2 Spring flower (5)

4 Geneva (anag.) (6)

5 Displeased (12)

6 Disentangle (7)

7 Absent-mindedness (13)

8 Boxing class (12)

14 Confused struggle (7)

16 Rich cake (6)

18 Covered with water (5)

CROSSWORD 443

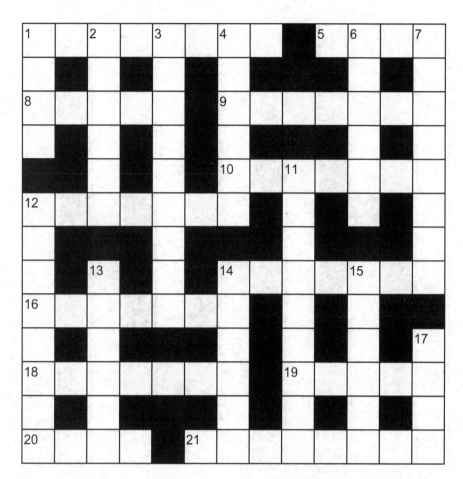

Across

1 Boring into (8)
5 Constituent (4)
8 Existing (5)
9 Reprimand (7)
10 Clothing (7)
12 Day of the week (7)
14 Ability to understand the feelings of another (7)
16 Relished (7)
18 Creepiest (7)
19 Insurgent or revolutionary (5)
20 Show excessive concern (4)
21 Anxiousness (8)

Down

1 Money that is owed (4)
2 Frozen water spear (6)
3 Pertaining to a fable (9)
4 Where one finds Oslo (6)
6 On a ship or train (6)
7 Study of the nature of God (8)
11 Medley of dried petals (9)
12 Unable to discern musical pitch (4-4)
13 Narrow sea inlets (6)
14 Amended (6)
15 Multiply by three (6)
17 Unfortunately (4)

Across

7 Isolated inlet of the sea (6)
8 Passenger ships (6)
9 Small green vegetables (4)
10 Absolute (8)
11 Marred (7)
13 Satiates (5)
15 Ring-shaped object (5)
16 Most tidy (7)
18 Least old (8)
19 Vertical spar on a ship (4)
21 Form-fitting garment (6)
22 Fame (6)

Down

1 Uncover; expose (4)
2 Awareness (13)
3 Asked to come along (7)
4 Hits with the hand (5)
5 Medication for allergies (13)
6 Recitals (anag.) (8)
12 Single-celled organisms (8)
14 Warming devices (7)
17 Thaws (5)
20 Sprinkled with seed (4)

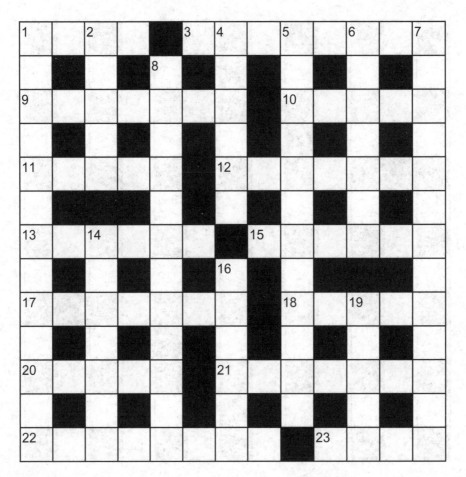

Across

1 Single article (4)

3 Gives strength to (8)

9 Grassy clump (7)

10 Mix up or confuse (5)

11 Ascended (5)

12 Settled oneself comfortably (7)

13 Happens (6)

15 Photographic equipment (6)

17 Permitted (7)

18 Precise (5)

20 Form of expression (5)

21 Tornado (7)

22 Loss of feeling (8)

23 Tiny social insects (4)

Down

1 Act of questioning (13)

2 Gets less difficult (5)

4 Mean (6)

5 Clearness (12)

6 Satisfy a desire (7)

7 Loyalty in the face of trouble (13)

8 Female fellow national (12)

14 Element needed by the body (7)

16 Proclamations (6)

19 Decorate (5)

Across

1 Cries (4)
3 12th month (8)
9 Suitor (7)
10 Military vehicles (5)
11 Science of deciphering codes (12)
14 Label (3)
16 Snake (5)
17 Seventh Greek letter (3)
18 First part of the Bible (3,9)
21 Loft (5)
22 Very odd (7)
23 More solitary (8)
24 Metal fastener (4)

Down

1 Ascot cat (anag.) (8)
2 Uneven (of a surface) (5)
4 What you hear with (3)
5 Lavish event (12)
6 Female spirit (7)
7 Optimistic (4)
8 Relating to numeric calculations (12)
12 Fun activities (5)
13 Title of a newspaper (8)
15 An edible jelly (7)
19 White waterbird (5)
20 Lofty (4)
22 Insect which collects pollen (3)

Across

7 Grisly (8)

8 Large stone (4)

9 Unable to hear (4)

10 Plant of the rose family (8)

11 Expressed audibly (7)

12 Crude (5)

15 Timber framework (5)

17 Slowly; sluggishly (7)

20 Temple dedicated to all the gods (8)

22 Prod (4)

23 Narrate (4)

24 Animated drawings (8)

Down

1 Take into custody (6)

2 Disregarding oneself (8)

3 Sea journeys (7)

4 Low dams (5)

5 Fill to capacity (4)

6 Perfumes (6)

13 Reassign (8)

14 Advertising placards (7)

16 Cried out (of a lion) (6)

18 Feeling of fondness (6)

19 Barrier (5)

21 Chat (4)

Across

1 Tiny parasite (4)
3 Force lifting something up (8)
9 Group of assistants (7)
10 Public square (5)
11 Item that unlocks a door (3)
12 Neatens (5)
13 Jollity (5)
15 Be alive; be real (5)
17 Threshold (5)
18 Sum charged (3)
19 Looking tired (5)
20 Closest (7)
21 Fade away (8)
22 Dairy product (4)

Down

1 Prescience (13)
2 Way in (5)
4 Like better (6)
5 Conjectural (12)
6 Dissimilar (7)
7 Party lanterns (anag.) (13)
8 Ineptness (12)
14 Brazilian dance (7)
16 Symbolic (6)
18 Muscular tissue (5)

Across

1 Positive and happy (6)

5 Very dirty (6)

8 Male hog (4)

9 Stimulate interest (8)

10 Stolen goods (5)

11 Winged angelic beings (7)

14 Inexplicable (13)

16 Wistfully thoughtful (7)

18 Thin pancake (5)

20 Device controlling flow of fuel to an engine (8)

22 Blood vessel (4)

23 Absorbent material (6)

24 Weaken a solution (6)

Down

2 Make the sound of a word (9)

3 Unpredictable (7)

4 Pack down tightly (4)

5 Retrieving (8)

6 Crowbar (5)

7 Smack (3)

12 Type of pen (9)

13 Small warship (8)

15 Act of turning up (7)

17 Exhibited (5)

19 First position (4)

21 Fruit of a rose (3)

Across

7 Unconditionally (13)

8 Reading quickly (8)

9 Donated (4)

10 Precipitating (7)

12 Armistice (5)

14 Drink copiously (5)

16 Waterlogged areas of land (7)

19 Sailing ship (4)

20 Teach (8)

22 Explanatory reason (13)

Down

1 Imprint (4)

2 Speech given in church (6)

3 Cosmetic liquids (7)

4 Birds use these to fly (5)

5 Cattle trough (6)

6 Collarbone (8)

11 11th sign of the zodiac (8)

13 Plunder (7)

15 Engages in combat (6)

17 Elf or fairy (6)

18 Short time (5)

21 Chef (4)

Across

1 One who makes beer (6)
7 Signal (8)
8 Marry (3)
9 Make worse (6)
10 Large wading bird (4)
11 Allowed by official rules (5)
13 Returns to a former state (7)
15 Fighting vessel (7)
17 Impress a pattern on (5)
21 Place where a wild animal lives (4)
22 Bidding (6)
23 Bustle (3)
24 Round (8)
25 Twinned (6)

Down

1 Lament (6)
2 Finishing (6)
3 Direct competitor (5)
4 Beautified (7)
5 The West (8)
6 Rigid; stern (6)
12 Theoretical (8)
14 Game played on a sloping board (7)
16 In slow tempo (of music) (6)
18 Writer (6)
19 Decorated with feathers (6)
20 Pointed; acute (5)

SOLUTIONS

Solution 1

Solution 2

Solution 3

Solution 4

Solution 5

Solution 6

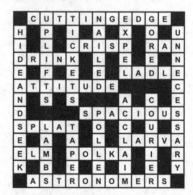

Solution 7

Solution 8

Solution 9

Solution 10

Solution 11

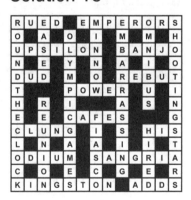

Solution 12

Solution 13

Solution 14

Solution 15

Solution 16

SOLUTIONS

Solution 17

Solution 18

Solution 19

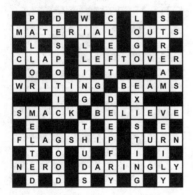

Solution 20

Solution 21

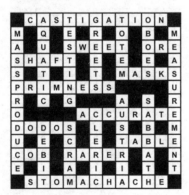

Solution 22

Solution 23

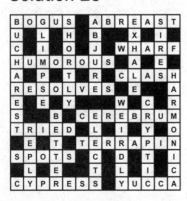

Solution 24

SOLUTIONS

Solution 25

Solution 26

Solution 27

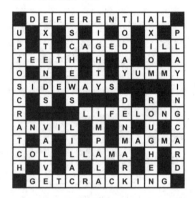

Solution 28

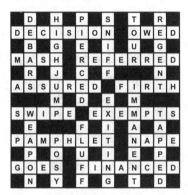

Solution 29

Solution 30

Solution 31

Solution 32

SOLUTIONS

Solution 33

Solution 34

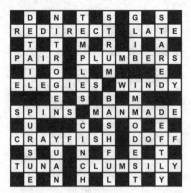

Solution 35

Solution 36

Solution 37

Solution 38

Solution 39

Solution 40

Solution 41

Solution 42

Solution 43

Solution 44

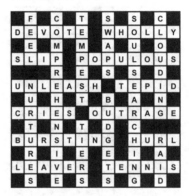

Solution 45

Solution 46

Solution 47

Solution 48

Solution 49

Solution 50

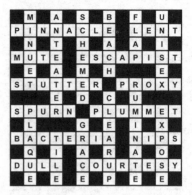

Solution 51

Solution 52

Solution 53

Solution 54

Solution 55

Solution 56

Solution 57

Solution 58

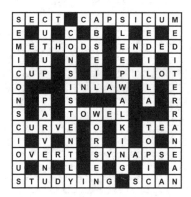

Solution 59

Solution 60

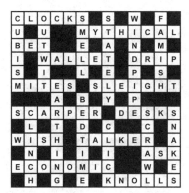

Solution 61

Solution 62

Solution 63

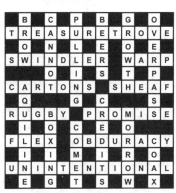

Solution 64

SOLUTIONS

Solution 65

Solution 66

Solution 67

Solution 68

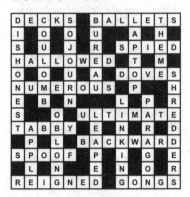

Solution 69

Solution 70

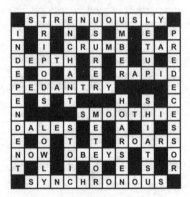

Solution 71

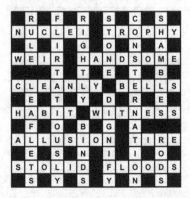

Solution 72

Solution 73

Solution 74

Solution 75

Solution 76

Solution 77

Solution 78

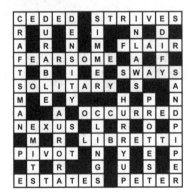

Solution 79

Solution 80

Solution 81

```
H O W L . A T L A N T I C
A . O . E H . D E . A . .
M A R I N E R . V I N E S
M . S . T E . E . A . E .
E N T E R T A I N I N G .
R . E . D T . T . I . . .
E U R O P E . K I S S E D
D . E . R D . T . . L . .
. U N V E R I F I A B L E
A . T . N M . O . R . N .
W E A V E . P L U M A G E
E . L . U . L . S . C . S
D I S O R D E R . K E G S
```

Solution 82

```
S T R A P . M A R I M B A
T . E . L . A . M . R . .
A D A G . S P E E D . . .
B O O S T I N G . O . A .
I . U . T E . A S I D E .
L I B R E T T O . E . X .
I . T . R . H . M . P . .
T . B E S C A L A T E . .
Y E A R N . E . N . S . R
. A . O . H I N D M O S T
G R A N D . Z . S . N . I
L . C . E . E . R . S . .
A S T O U N D . T H Y M E
```

Solution 83

```
L O O N . S P L A S H E S
I . X . D A . F . U . E .
G A B R I E L . F I N A L
H . O . S A . E . D . F .
T O W . H C . C U R I A .
F . . E X E R T . E . W .
I . C A . . I . D . A . .
N . H . R E T R O . . R .
G R E E T . H . N . T E E
E . R . E . R . A . R . N
R A V E N . O U T D A T E
E . I . E . W . E . I . S
D E L U D I N G . A L P S
```

Solution 84

```
I T C H . C L E A R C U T
N . R . U . O . D . H . E
C L E A N U P . V E I N S
U . D . C . A . C . T . .
B R O T H E R I N L A W .
A . . A . O . T . G . C .
T U G . R U M B A . O W L
E . R . I . A . G . . U .
. C A N T A N K E R O U S
A . D . A . O . P . T . .
P L U M B . S H U T E Y E
E . A . L . E . S . R . .
S O L V E N C Y . E A R S
```

Solution 85

```
H A P P I E S T . F E E T
I . L . N . A . N . V . I
V A U L T . Y . A H E A D
E . M . R . I . R . R . I
. . C O U N T R Y M A N .
P . R . D . G . O . O . E
R U E F U L . S W O R D S
O . S . C . S . M . E . S
H Y P O T H E S I S . . .
I . O . I . N . N . D . M
B I N G O . O . D R A P E
I . S . N . R . E . W . M
T H E N . F A N D A N G O
```

Solution 86

```
. M . C . T . B . C . N .
B E F O R E . L A R V A E
. S . M . A . U . Y . V .
C H U M . S Y N O P S I S
. . E . I . T . T . G . .
F A W N I N G . F O R A Y
. T . S . G . P . G . T .
S H O U T . C U R R I E S
. L . R . S . T . A . . .
R E C A L L E D . P O P S
. T . B . I . O . H . A .
P I G L E T . W E E K L Y
. C . E . S . N . R . E .
```

Solution 87

```
I M B U E D . R . S . R .
M . E . A C A N T H U S .
P O D . I . D . A . N . .
A . B O N S A I . R A N D
C . U . Y . C . G . E . .
T O G A S . C A V A L R Y
. . N . T . L . Z . . . .
S A F A R I S . D E L F T
. R . C . P . H . E . R .
V E T O . T H E F T S . I
. N . N . O . I . . I M P
B A L D N E S S . . O . O
. S . A . S . T A N N E D
```

Solution 88

```
. C U L M I N A T I O N .
H . N . O . E . A . R . A
A . I . P L A N K . B I G
R E C A P . R . E . I . G
P . O . I E . N A T A L .
S E R E N A D E . . O . .
I . N . G . . F . G . M .
C . . A P E R T U R E . .
H E W E R . O . A . N . R
O . O . U . P . Z E B R A
R A M . L A P A Z . O . T
D . A . E . E . L . A . E
. I N G R E D I E N T S .
```

Solution 89

Solution 90

Solution 91

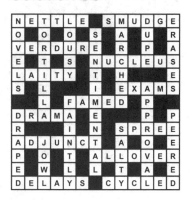

Solution 92

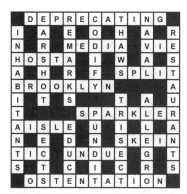

Solution 93

Solution 94

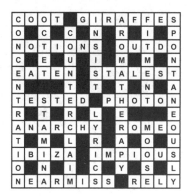

Solution 95

Solution 96

Solution 97

Solution 98

Solution 99

Solution 100

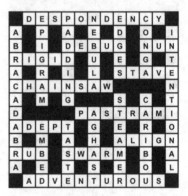

Solution 101

Solution 102

Solution 103

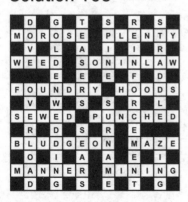

Solution 104

Solution 105

Solution 106
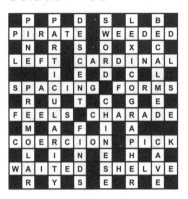

Solution 107

Solution 108

Solution 109
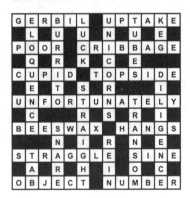

Solution 110
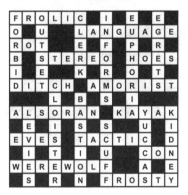

Solution 111

Solution 112

SOLUTIONS

Solution 113

Solution 114

Solution 115

Solution 116

Solution 117

Solution 118

Solution 119

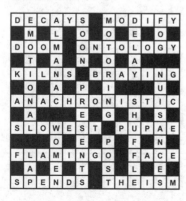

Solution 120

Solution 121

Solution 122

Solution 123

Solution 124

Solution 125

Solution 126

Solution 127

Solution 128

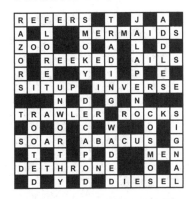

SOLUTIONS

Solution 129

Solution 130

Solution 131

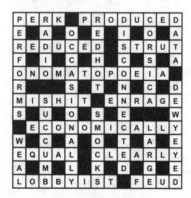

Solution 132

Solution 133

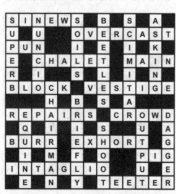

Solution 134

Solution 135

Solution 136

Solution 137

Solution 138

Solution 139

Solution 140

Solution 141

Solution 142

Solution 143

Solution 144

SOLUTIONS

Solution 145

Solution 146

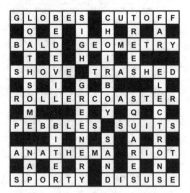

Solution 147

Solution 148

Solution 149

Solution 150

Solution 151

Solution 152

Solution 153

Solution 154

Solution 155

Solution 156

Solution 157

Solution 158

Solution 159

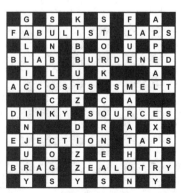

Solution 160

SOLUTIONS

Solution 161

Solution 162

Solution 163

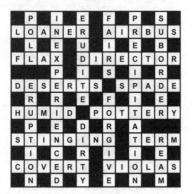

Solution 164

Solution 165

Solution 166

Solution 167

Solution 168

Solution 169

```
S I G H T S   C L O S E T
A   Y   O   M   A   E   R
F O R M U L A   P   A   A
E   A   R   S E T T L E S
L U T E S   T   O     H
Y   I     E   P I C K Y
  O   K A R T S   O
W I N C E   P     N   A
I     R   I   D I C E D
R E T R A C E   E   E   J
I   R   T   C A L Y P S O
N     I   I   E   T   I
G E M I N I   R A I S I N
```

Solution 170

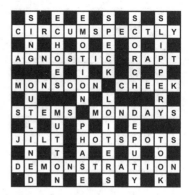

```
  S   E   E   S   S     S
C I R C U M S P E C T L Y
  N   H   O   E   O     I
A G N O S T I C   R A P T
  E     I   K   C   P
M O N S O O N   C H E E K
U     N   L       R
S T E M S   M O N D A Y S
L   U   P   I   E
J I L T   H O T S P O T S
N     T   A   E   U   O
D E M O N S T R A T I O N
  D   N   E   S   Y   K
```

Solution 171

```
W E A K E N E D   T R A P
O   B   N   A   A     E
O I L E D   S T I F F E N
D   A   U   I   F   C
  Z   R   E N G L I S H
O P E N A I R   U   A   A
I     N       A     N
N   A   C   A C R O B A T
T A B L E T S   A   A
M   I     S   N   N   H
E N D G A M E   T I T L E
N   E     T   E   A   R
T O S S   E S T E E M E D
```

Solution 172

```
  D E L I C I O U S L Y
T   N   N   R   S   I   G
R   G   F A I T H   B A R
A W A R E   S   E   R   A
C   G   R   E   R E A P S
K E E N N E S S       S
R   D   O     I   I   H
E       F L A M E N C O
C A L M S   O   P   H   P
O   E   O   C   U S U R P
R O D   L E A S T   M   E
D   G   V   L   E   A   R
  N E V E R E N D I N G
```

Solution 173

```
C O M E T S   D   S   A
O   A     P R E T T I F Y
V A N   E   S   O     R
E   T U R N U P   C U E S
R   R   D   O   K   S
S H A M E   P I R A N H A
    A   T   L   D
C A P S T A N   W E D G E
  N   S   S   B     E   X
O G R E   S T E P U P   C
  O   U   E   A     O W E
W R E S T L E R     S   E
  A   E   S   D E P E N D
```

Solution 174

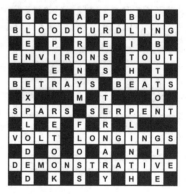

```
  G   C   A   P   B   U
B L O O D C U R D L I N G
  E   P   R   E   I   B
E N V I R O N S   T O U T
      E   N   S   H   T
B E T R A Y S   B E A T S
X   M   T       O
S P A R S   S E R P E N T
L   E   F   R   L
V O L T   L O N G I N G S
D   O   O   A   N   I
D E M O N S T R A T I V E
  D   K   S   Y   H   E
```

Solution 175

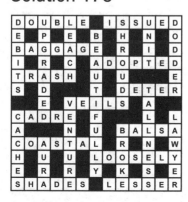

```
D O U B L E   I S S U E D
E   P   E   B   H   N   O
B A G G A G E   R   I   D
I   R   C   A D O P T E D
T R A S H   U   U     E
S   D   T   D E T E R
  E   V E I L S   A
C A D R E   F     L   L
A     N   U   B A L S A
C O A S T A L   R   N   W
H   U   U   L O O S E L Y
E   R   R   Y   K   S   E
S H A D E S   L E S S E R
```

Solution 176

```
D U C T   P R E C E P T S
E   L   U   O   A   A   U
F L O U N C E   R A T E D
E   W   D     D   E   S
C O N T E M P T I B L E
T     R   R   O   L   C
O U T   G H O U L   A D O
R   O   A   W   O     O
  A S T R O L O G I C A L
E   S   M   I   H   N
T R I P E   C A S C A D E
N   N   N   O   T   S   S
A N G S T R O M   N E W S
```

SOLUTIONS

Solution 177

Solution 178

Solution 179

Solution 180

Solution 181

Solution 182

Solution 183

Solution 184

Solution 185

Solution 186

Solution 187

Solution 188

Solution 189

Solution 190

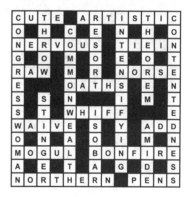

Solution 191

Solution 192

SOLUTIONS

Solution 193

Solution 194
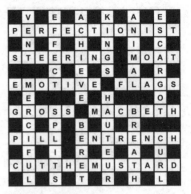

Solution 195
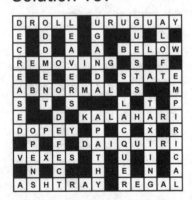

Solution 196
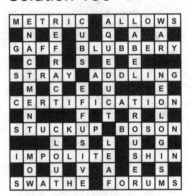

Solution 197
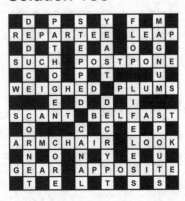

Solution 198

Solution 199

Solution 200
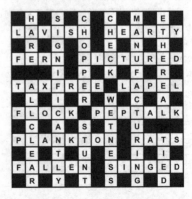

SOLUTIONS

Solution 201

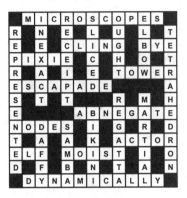

Solution 202

Solution 203

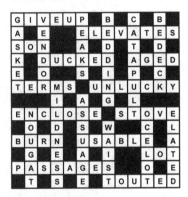

Solution 204

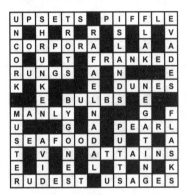

Solution 205

Solution 206

Solution 207

Solution 208

SOLUTIONS

Solution 209

Solution 210

Solution 211

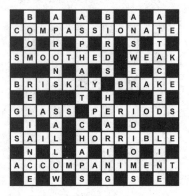

Solution 212

Solution 213

Solution 214

Solution 215

Solution 216

Solution 217

Solution 218

Solution 219

Solution 220

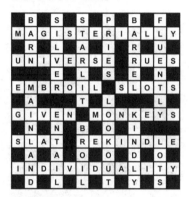

Solution 221

Solution 222

Solution 223

Solution 224

SOLUTIONS

Solution 225

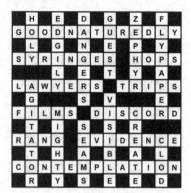

Solution 226

Solution 227

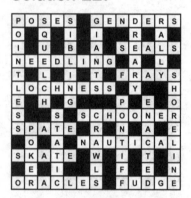

Solution 228

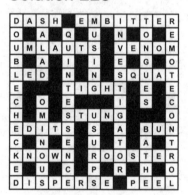

Solution 229

Solution 230

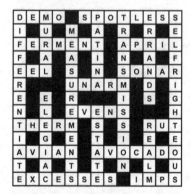

Solution 231

Solution 232

Solution 233

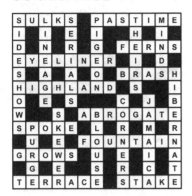

Solution 234

Solution 235

Solution 236

Solution 237

Solution 238

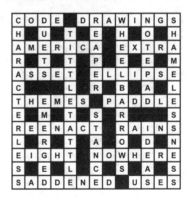

Solution 239

Solution 240

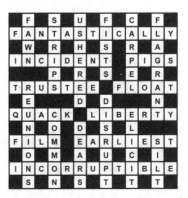

SOLUTIONS

Solution 241

Solution 242

Solution 243

Solution 244

Solution 245

Solution 246

Solution 247

Solution 248

Solution 249

Solution 250

Solution 251

Solution 252

Solution 253

Solution 254

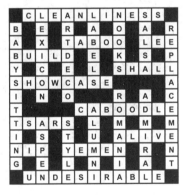

Solution 255

Solution 256

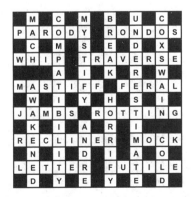

SOLUTIONS

Solution 257

Solution 258

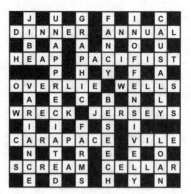

Solution 259

Solution 260

Solution 261

Solution 262

Solution 263

Solution 264

Solution 265

Solution 266

Solution 267

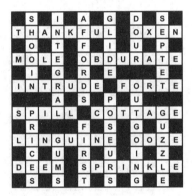

Solution 268

Solution 269

Solution 270

Solution 271

Solution 272

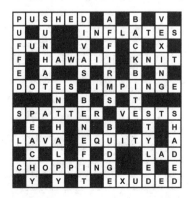

Solution 273

Solution 274

Solution 275

Solution 276

Solution 277

Solution 278

Solution 279

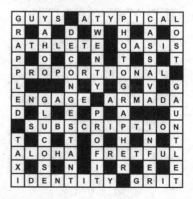

Solution 280

Solution 281

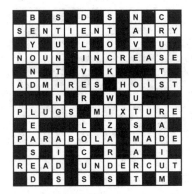

Solution 282

Solution 283

Solution 284

Solution 285

Solution 286

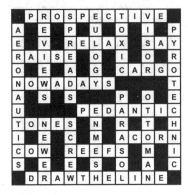

Solution 287

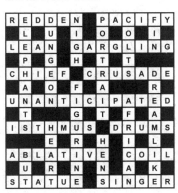

Solution 288

Solution 289

Solution 290

Solution 291

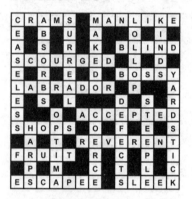

Solution 292

Solution 293

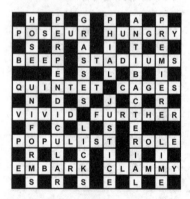

Solution 294

Solution 295

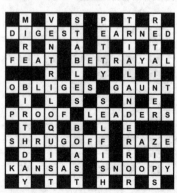

Solution 296

Solution 297

Solution 298

Solution 299

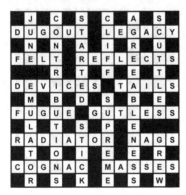

Solution 300

Solution 301

Solution 302

Solution 303

Solution 304

SOLUTIONS

Solution 305

Solution 306

Solution 307

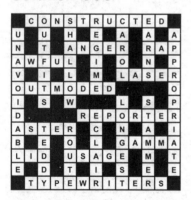

Solution 308

Solution 309

Solution 310

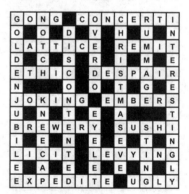

Solution 311

Solution 312

Solution 313

Solution 314

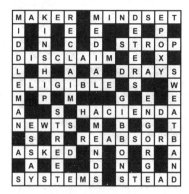

Solution 315

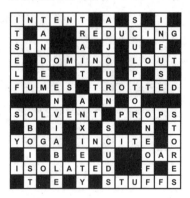

Solution 316

Solution 317

Solution 318

Solution 319

Solution 320

SOLUTIONS

Solution 321

```
M E T A L S   A   O   G
I   U   M A N F U L L Y
M U M   A   Y   T   I
I   B E D L A M   W I T S
C   L   L   O   E   C
S H E E P   F R E I G H T
      X   T   E   G
A P P E A R S   C H A R D
  R   M   I   B   P   U
D A M P   V I R A G O   R
  N   T   I   E   G A B
S C H E M A T A   E   A
  E   D   L   M O D E R N
```

Solution 322

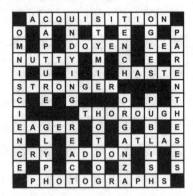

Solution 323

```
T H I N S   S A Y I N G S
R   C   W   O   N   R
I   I   E L   S C R A P
M A C K E R E L   U   Z
E   L   T   M   C R E E K
S E E D L I N G   S   N
T   S   Y   O   E   O
E   A   P A N D E M I C
R A C E D   D   D   P   K
  B   R   D O W N L O A D
P U P I L   P   E   W   O
  Z   A   T   S   E   W
A Z A L E A S   S I R E N
```

Solution 324

Solution 325

Solution 326

Solution 327

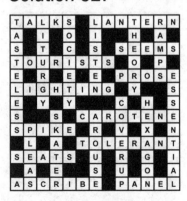

Solution 328

Solution 329

Solution 330

Solution 331

Solution 332

Solution 333

Solution 334

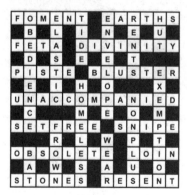

Solution 335

Solution 336

SOLUTIONS

Solution 337

Solution 338

Solution 339

Solution 340

Solution 341

Solution 342

Solution 343

Solution 344

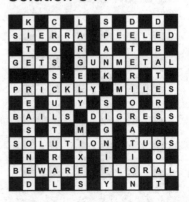

Solution 345

Solution 346

Solution 347

Solution 348

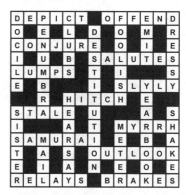

Solution 349

Solution 350

Solution 351

Solution 352

Solution 353

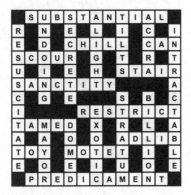

Solution 354

Solution 355

Solution 356

Solution 357

Solution 358

Solution 359

Solution 360

Solution 361

Solution 362

Solution 363

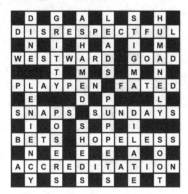

Solution 364

Solution 365

Solution 366

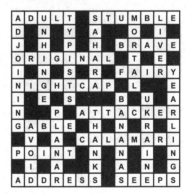

Solution 367

Solution 368

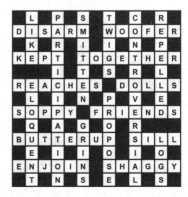

Solution 369

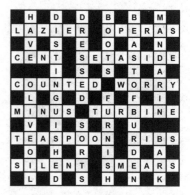

Solution 370

Solution 371

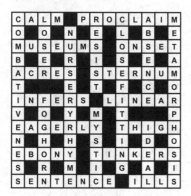

Solution 372

Solution 373

Solution 374

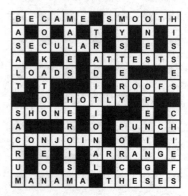

Solution 375

Solution 376

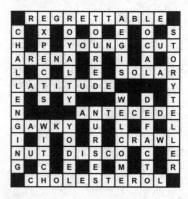

Solution 377

Solution 378

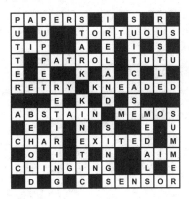

Solution 379

Solution 380

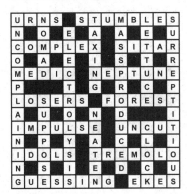

Solution 381

Solution 382

Solution 383

Solution 384

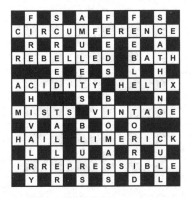

Solution 385

Solution 386

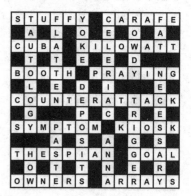

Solution 387

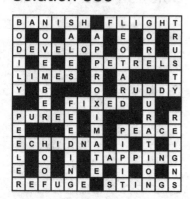

Solution 388

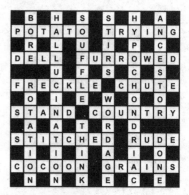

Solution 389

Solution 390

Solution 391

Solution 392

Solution 393

Solution 394

Solution 395

Solution 396

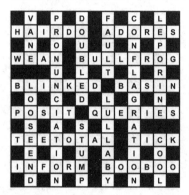

Solution 397

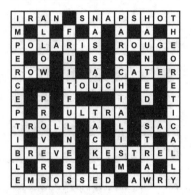

Solution 398

Solution 399

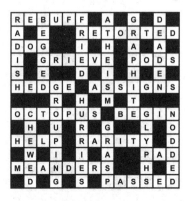

Solution 400

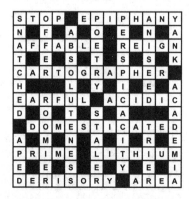

SOLUTIONS

Solution 401

D	E	C	I	D	E		S	T	Y	L	E	S
I		O		I		R		O		O		H
V	A	L	A	N	C	E		N		A		O
I		E		G		S	H	I	M	M	E	R
D	U	S	T	Y		E		G				E
E		L				M		H	O	U	R	S
		A		C	U	B	I	T		D		
B	O	W	E	R		L		D		S		
A		U		A		C	R	E	S	T		
C	E	S	S	I	O	N		L		R		O
K		E		S		C	R	E	E	P	E	R
E		A		E		E		A		I		K
R	E	T	O	R	T		S	T	A	N	D	S

Solution 402

Solution 403

Solution 404

Solution 405

Solution 406

Solution 407

Solution 408

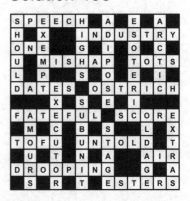

Solution 409

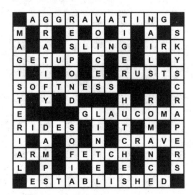

Solution 410

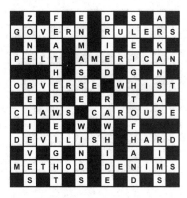

Solution 411

Solution 412

Solution 413

Solution 414

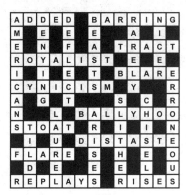

Solution 415

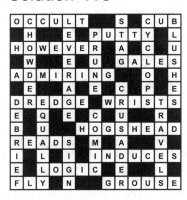

Solution 416

SOLUTIONS

Solution 417

Solution 418

Solution 419

Solution 420

Solution 421

Solution 422

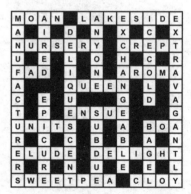

Solution 423

Solution 424

Solution 425

Solution 426

Solution 427

Solution 428

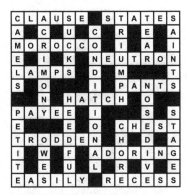

Solution 429

Solution 430

Solution 431

Solution 432

Solution 433

Solution 434

Solution 435

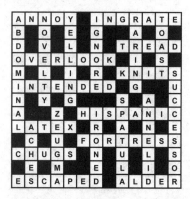

Solution 436

Solution 437

Solution 438

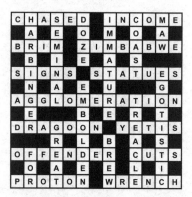

Solution 439

Solution 440

Solution 441

```
M I M E D # P R O F U S E
A # A # I # R # O # H # #
G # S # G # I # T R E A T
N I C K N A M E # M # V #
I # A # I # A # C A M E L
F O R E T E L L # L # I #
I # A # Y # # B # A # G #
E # # S # G H O U L I S H
S P I K Y # E # Z # R # T
# L # I # M A R Z I P A N
Q U A I L # V # I # O # E
# S # N # # E # N # R # S
C H A G R I N # G A T E S
```

Solution 442

Solution 443

```
D R I L L I N G # P A R T
E # C # E # O # # B # H #
B E I N G # R E P R O V E
T # C # E # W # # # A # O
# # # L # N # A P P A R E L
T U E S D A Y # O # D # O
O # # # A # # # T # # # G
N # F # R # E M P A T H Y
E N J O Y E D # O # R # #
D # O # # # I # U # E # A
E E R I E S T # R E B E L
A # D # # # E # R # L # A
F U S S # E D G I N E S S
```

Solution 444

Solution 445

Solution 446

Solution 447

Solution 448

Solution 449

Solution 450

Solution 451